TALES OF A
MEANDERING
MEDIC

11.11.2021

This copy of my Memoir is
gifted to Mr Ian Hislop

S P Gubran

DR. SIMON GIBSON

TALES OF A MEANDERING MEDIC

Ordering Information:

BookTrail Agency
8838 Sleepy Hollow Rd.
Kansas City, MO 64114

Printed in the United States of America

CONTENTS

THIS WORK IS DEDICATED TO

MY BELOVED DAUGHTER S
AND MY BEST FRIEND TES

THIS WORK IS DEFINETLY NOT
DEDICATED TO THE DVLA AND
THE GMC
Dr S P Gibson BA MB ChB MA MRCP FPCert T(GP) MD
FRCP
RETIRED CONSULTANT
PHYSICIAN and
NEPHROLOGIST

BA = Bachelor of Arts University College Oxford University
MB ChB = Basic medical qualification Sheffield University Medical School
MA = Master of Arts University College Oxford University
MRCP = Member of the Royal College of Physicians
FPCert = Family Planning Certificate
T(GP) = Doctor Trained to work as a GP in general practice
MD = Doctor of Medicine Sheffield University Medical School
FRCP = Fellow of the Royal College of Physicians

And the above is what I call my "Full Monty"

GLOSSARY

Medicine is full of abbreviations and acronyms. Hopefully, the list below is comprehensive.

A   Arrogance. Seems to be endemic (not pandemic) amongst CEOs of monolithic organizations eg. Ms Julie Lennard CEO of Driver and Vehicle Licensing Autocracy, Mr Charlie Messey CEO of Gang of Mealy-mouthed Charlatans-previously known as General Medical Council

B   BVH – Blackpool Victoria Hospital
BDGH – Bury District General Hospital
BH – Barrow Hospital (Furness General Hospital)
BS – See Definitions below

C   CAPD – Continuous Ambulatory Peritoneal Dialysis
CVVH – Continuous Veno-Venous Haemofiltration
CDGH – Chorley District General Hospital
Charlie who may be a charlie CEO Gang of Mealy-mouthed Charlatans

D   DVLA – Driver and Vehicle Licensing Authority Driver and Vehicle Licensing Autocracy
DU – Dialysis Unit

F   FDGH – Furness District General Hospital (Barrow Hospital)

G   GH – General Hospital
GMC – General Medical Council Gang of Mealy-mouthed Charlatans

H   Health
Home
Hospital HO House Officer Haemodialysis
Home Haemodialysis HD

I   Intensive Care Unit ICU Intensive Therapy Unit ITU
Ivory Tower (home of DVLA in Swansea)

L   LP Lumbar Puncture

N   NHS – National Health Service. The greatest health care institution in the UK, in Europe, in the World, in the Solar System, in the Universe. And it saved my life.

P   Peritoneal CAPD
PP – Pompous Pillock

S   Senior House Officer
        SIT – Smaller Ivory Tower (home of GMC in London), but they have multiple very small ivory towers spread throughout UK
        SPR – Specialist Registrar, a medical or surgical registrar, who has specialized in a particular branch of medicine or surgery, eg, chest medicine or ophthalmic surgery.

T   Therapy

U   Unit

W   WGH Westmoreland General Hospital, Kendal Hospital

DEFINITIONS
(FROM CONCISE OXFORD DICTIONARY 9TH EDITION)

Autocracy – absolute government by one individual

Charlatan – a person falsely claiming a special knowledge or skill

Charlie – a fool

Mealy-mouthed – afraid to use plain expression

BS – (from Collin's on-line Dictionary)

> 1 Countable Noun
>   A BS or B.S. is a first degree from a college or university. BS is an abbreviation for Bachelor of Science
> 2 Countable Noun
>   A BS or B.S. is written after someone's name to indicate that they have a BS
> 3 Uncountable Noun
>   If you describe something as BS or B.S., you are saying that it is nonsense or completely untrue. BS is an abbreviation for bullshit

NEPHROLOGIST = Kidney Doctor

CONSULTANT = a Doctor who has climbed to the top of the greasy pole

ACKNOWLEDGEMENTS

I am very grateful to:

My parents for creating me, and sustaining me, and instilling in me values that have sustained me throughout my life (RIP Mum and Dad).

Mr A, Consultant Neurosurgeon, and his team at Royal Preston Hospital for giving me my life back. I have improved progressively since neurosurgery on 4.12.19.

Tes who was there for me in my darkest hours.

S, my beloved daughter. Always an inspiration.

My family. Always supportive.

My neighbours (see vignette My Neighbours).

The NHS for providing me with employment. And when I needed help, was there for me.

Mel and her staff at Lantern over the Lune café, Glasson Dock. As well as excellent food, the environment was therapeutic. Mel also reviewed some of my work. A mother of 5, she had plenty of experience of life.

The Pear Tree café at Ashton Hall Garden Centre. Excellent food in great surroundings.

Mr Les Wilkinson, the truest of true friends. Always there. Always supportive.

Ms Cat Smith, my local Lancaster MP. The DVL Autocracy ignored her as they ignored me.

Preston Magistrates Court. They answered the phone promptly. My e-mails too. And the DVL Autocracy was due to appear there, but caved and returned my driving license to me, two months late.

The DVLAutocracy could ignore me, my local MP too. But they could not ignore the Courts. My advice to anyone who is struggling with the DVLAutocracy, is to use the Courts.

Baroness Cumberlege, my inspirational friend in a high place. The House of Lords. She is the BCC in most of my e-mails to monolithic bullying bureaucracies.

Dame Julie Mellor, OBE, for her very revealing, and sad, report on the DVLAutocracy, published and available to the public in 2018. And in spite of her clear recommendations, the DVLAutocracy has not changed. And based on my experiences, they seem to have got worse, much worse.

My former patients, and the very kind things they wrote about me in the retirement cards they sent me. Sometimes I read them again. To remind me that I was a highly competent, inspirational Consultant Physician and Nephrologist. Always kind, caring, empathic, and compassionate. And honest about their renal situation.

SUMMARY

This book describes my journey through my working life as a Doctor.

It also describes my experiences as a patient, and the wonderful life saving care I received from the NHS.

There are also a few lines on my earlier life, as a Medical Student and how that impacted on my life as a Hospital Consultant Physician and Nephrologist (kidney specialist).

The book consists of a series of vignettes describing episodes that have lingered in my memory.

This is well illustrated by the vignette " A Legacy of Spina bifida". In this, I describe a courageous lady with spina bifida. Illustrations come mainly from Bing Pictures, although some are of my own creation.

There is a detailed Glossary at the start of the book explaining abbreviations commonly used in Medicine, for example LP is the abbreviation for Lumbar Puncture, used in the vignette describing my own lumbar puncture.

Towards the end of the book I describe my interaction with the Driving and Vehicle Licensing Authority (Autocracy), and the General Medical Council (Gang of Mealy mouthed Charlatans).

Hopefully the book will entertain and educate. The intended reader is an average member of the public and no prior medical knowledge is required. Some over inflated egos may be punctured.

So Reader, enjoy "Tales of a Meandering Medic".

Any profits will be donated to Oxfam. I have been a donor to Oxfam since my undergraduate days at Oxford.

THE PRE-MEDIC MEANDERINGS (MY EARLY LIFE)

I arrived in the world in 1954, in Fleetwood.

My Father (RIP Dad) was an itinerant civil engineer. A very brave man: was awarded the MC in the field at the Battle of Monte Casino.

My Mother (RIP Mum) was a long suffering home maker.

The family (I have 2 older brothers) lived in a caravan. My father (Rip Dad) had decided that the only way to keep the family together, and him work at various locations, was for us to live in a caravan, and move it from site to site. He was working on Fleetwood sea wall when I appeared.

I think my mother (RIP Mum) decided that caring for three rapidly developing boys in a caravan was unrealistic. And so we moved into a semi-in Crosby, which is a coastal town midway between Liverpool and Southport. Crosby is perhaps only notable for the Gormley Iron Men Statues, and good schools.

We were all fortunate to pass the 11-Plus, and gained admission to St Mary's College, a Roman Catholic Grammar School. My late mother (Rip Mum) was a devout Catholic, and hoped her three sons would be similarly devout. She was disappointed. But my immediate brother is married to a C of E Rector!!

My parents (RIP Mum and Dad) were keen on education. Their attitudes predated Mr Tony Blair's education education education philosophy by 50 years.

We passed through the educational system.

All three of us gained admission to University College, Oxford University, two of us winning Scholarships.

My eldest brother read Medicine and became an eye surgeon. My immediate brother read History and joined the Civil Service. I read Natural Sciences, but realized that I too wished to study Medicine and so after completing my Oxford degree, I moved to Sheffield University Medical School.

The rest, as you might say, is history!!

THE MEANDERINGS

ROTHERAM 1.8.81---31.1.82 House Officer Surgery

SHEFFIELD 1.2.82---31.7.82 House Officer General and Renal Medicine

LEICESTER 1.8.82--21.5.83 Senior House Officer Pathology and Accident and Emergency Medicine

COVENTRY 22.5.83---21.5.85 Senior House Officer Medicine

BURY 1.8.85---31.1.86 Senior House Officer Obstetrics and Gynaecology with clinics in RAMSBOTTOM and RAWTENSTALL

KENILWORTH 1.2.86---31.1.87 Training year in General Practice including family planning training in LEAMINGTON SPA

EAST BIRMINGHAM HOSPITAL 17.2.87---31.10.87 Registrar in Chest medicine

EAST BIRMINGHAM HOSPITAL 1.11.87---31.10.88 Registrar in Nephrology and General Medicine

EAST BIRMINGHAM HOSPITAL 1.11.88---20.5.91 Research Fellow in Nephrology and multiple locum GP sessions at YARDLEY GREEN HEALTH CENTRE, and a few in SOLIHULL and HENLEY IN ARDEN.

Locum sessions in General Practices in the EAST MIDLANDS and continued research activity at EAST BIRMINGHAM HOSPITAL 1.6.91---31.12.91

EAST BIRMINGHAM HOSPITAL 1.1.92---15.11.92 Registrar in Nephrology

BIRMIGHAM UINIVERSITY and EAST BIRMINGHAM HOSPITAL 16.11.92---28.2.1993 Temporary Lecturer and Locum Senior Registrar in Diabetes, Endocrinology and General Medicine

EAST BIRMINGHAM HOSPITAL 1.3.93---30.4.93 Locum Consultant in Nephrology and General Medicine

Writing up research and short locum appointments 1.5.93---29.7.93

COVENTRY 30.7.93---29.12.93 Locum Consultant in Nephrology and General Medicine Walsgrave Hospital

WOLVERHAMPTON 24.1.94---31.1.94 Locum Consultant in Nephrology and General Medicine New Cross Hospital

Dr. Simon Gibson

BRISTOL 1.2.94---30.6.94 Locum Senior Registrar in Nephrology Southmead Renal Unit

BRISTOL 1.7.94---27.9.94 Locum Consultant in Nephrology Southmead Renal Unit

CARDIFF ROYAL INFIRMARY 1.10.94---16.4.95 Locum Senior Registrar in Nephrology and General Medicine

BRISTOL 18.4.95---7.7.95 Locum Senior Registrar in Nephrology Southmead Renal Unit

BRISTOL 8.7.95---15.6.96 Senior Registrar Nephrology and General Medicine

PRESTON 16.6.96------------- CONSULTANT PHYSICIAN AND NEPHROLOGIST !!!!!

But the meanderings did not stop. My post included establishing a completely new renal service for LANCASTER, KENDAL and BARROW. But the meanderings were only day trips.

It would take 1---1.2 hrs.to reach Barrow and 1---1.2 hrs to return to my Lancaster home (the Renal Clinic was all day). Happy Days, sort of.

And all these meanderings with inevitable exams produced my Full Monty: BA MB ChB MA MRCP FPCert T(GP) MD FRCP

MY EXAM FAILURES

AS A MEDICAL STUDENT

I attended Sheffield University Medical School from 1976-1981.
I failed an anatomy exam but passed it on the re-sit.

AS A DOCTOR

MRCP X 1.

The MRCP (Membership of the Royal College of Physicians) is the gateway exam to Higher Medical Training (HMT). You cannot climb the greasy pole of HMT without it. The exam has 2 parts: a written, which is a multiple choice paper, done at the Royal College of Physicians headquarters in London, and a practical. For the practical candidates could be sent anywhere in the UK. The practical consisted of "short cases" and a "long case".

I was working as a Senior House Officer at the Walsgrave Hospital Coventry, when I made my first attempt.

At my first attempt, I think the written bit was ok.

For the practical, I was sent to an alien land, 100s of miles from my Kenilworth home: Scotland (!). The Hospital was a small District General about 30 miles from Glasgow. I think my short cases went well. But the long case was a disaster. The patient was an alcoholic with a very strong Scottish accent. I struggled to understand him, so my attempt to get a medical history from him did not go well. My examiners were Scottish, and so they did not have a problem with his accent. I think my examination of the patient was ok. He had an enlarged liver as many alcoholics do.

I failed. But I received no feedback. Perhaps the examiners did not like my English accent !!

I was doing my GP training year in Kenilwoth when I made my second attempt. The written bit of the exam went well.

For the practical, I was sent to St. Thomas Hospital London. This is where PM Mr Boris Johnson was admitted with Covid 19. No problems with accents there ! No problems with my short cases and long case. I passed, and I was entitled to put MRCP after my name.

DCH x 1.

DCH stands for Diploma in Child Health. Sat this in Manchester. Don't know why I failed. No feedback. Did not resit. Thought being a Doctor/Parent was reasonable training in Child Health.

MD x 2.
READER BEWARE. MY STRUGGLE TO GAIN MY MD IS A MINI SAGA !!

The MD is a research based degree, often done part-time, while NHS work continues. Usually hospital doctors study for an MD, but I think very occasionally GPs do too. The title of my MD Thesis was "Studies on Erythropoiesis in Dialysis Patients". My research work was done at East Birmingham Hospital (now renamed: Birmingham Heartlands Hospital).Half of my salary was paid by the NHS, the other half was paid by the East Birmingham Hospital Renal Research Fund. The time period was October 1988 to March 1992.

My research involved work with the transformative drug erythropoietin (EPO). It is almost certainly true that EPO is the biggest therapeutic advance for those with the anemia of ESRF (End Stage Renal Failure), since dialysis became available. It is not cheap. See vignette titled " The Good The Bad and the very very ugly (Goodpastures Syndrome)". It can totally transform the lives of those unfortunate enough to need dialysis.

I made my first attempt to gain my MD in January 2001. I failed and rightly so. My Thesis was poor. I did not include all the appropriate references etc, etc, etc. I appealed against the decision, because I knew that the clinical work that I had done was good. My appeal was successful.

Time passed and I continued with my research and NHS work. I submitted my second attempt in June 2002. Again I failed. Not sure why this time. No feedback from examiners.

I appealed again. My appeal was again successful. New supervisors were appointed. I continued with my research and NHS work.

Under the guidance of my new supervisors, I totally reorganized the presentation of my Thesis.

I submitted my third attempt in September 2005. A grueling Oral Examination followed. And on 19.4.2007 I had very good news from Sheffield University Medical School. I HAD PASSED MY MD !!

My progress up the greasy pole of hospital medicine could continue, if I chose to continue the climb.

I AM NOT A QUITTER.

MY NEIGHBOURS

My neurosurgery took place on Friday 4.12.19 at Royal Preston Hospital and I returned home on Monday 7.12.19.

The awful stiffness in my legs gradually improved but it took much longer for my balance.

For food supplies, I embraced on-line shopping, as I had done prior to surgery. I ordered provisions on-line and kept myself fed and hydrated.

Christmas was approaching and I wanted to get on and sort out Christmas cards.

But I could not walk to the nearest Post Box. And similarly I could not drive as my license had been suspended for 6 months.

To the rescue Emeritus Professor KD, and his equally erudite wife. They collected mail from my house and took it to the Post Box. They also purchased stamps and additional cards on my behalf.

Emeritus Prof KD and Mrs D were also hugely helpful by reviewing my vignettes and making helpful suggestions on how they might be improved. Neither have any medical background and my book is aimed at such.

Mr and Mrs J and T M were helpful in so many ways. The reality of internet shopping is that you forget to order something, or you run out of something before the next. One text to Mrs TM, and the problem was solved. Within 24 hours the deficit in my supplies was eliminated. Mr and Mrs J and T M have 2 delightful children, aged 6 and 10. Young blood in a colony of crumblies. The arrival of the M family in CC, lowered the average age of CC inhabitants by 20 years. As a small thank you, I provided a 24 hr a day emergency service for their son, who is asthmatic. My trusty stethoscope was placed near my front-door, ready for immediate use.

Mr I and Mrs B M Shephard, the most senior residents of CC, were a pillar of strength. Always welcoming and always supportive. Mr S has a number of health issues including high blood pressure. To repay in a very small way, I checked his BP on a few occasions. And I had a letter published in the Daily Telegraph about this. See next page for the letter.

There were others too. I am grateful to them all.

DAILY TELEGRAPH

13.10.20

Volunteer nurse

SIR - An elderly neighbour had his blood pressure medicine changed by his GP, but there was no follow-up to see if the new dosage was correct, or if there were side effects.

As a retired physician, I dusted off my old machine and have been checking his blood pressure. It has been mutually beneficial as it has eased my isolation (I live alone).

Fortunately, the dose was correct and there have been no side effects.

Dr S P Gibson
Aldcliffe, Lancashire

MY COVENTRY YEARS PART 1

GULSON HOSPITAL COVENTRY featuring: THE PARKING ABUSERS and THE BURGLAR AND THE OILY DRAINPIPE

I had decided that for the time being I would pursue a career in Hospital Medicine and I managed to secure an SHO training rotation in Coventry. The rotation was between Gulson Hospital and the Walsgrave Hospital.

Even if I opted to be a GP, the training would be valuable.

What particularly attracted me to the Walsgrave was that it had a staff swimming pool. At that time I was a swimming obsessive !!

Gulson Hospital was an inner city Hospital, providing medical and surgical services (Internet trawling revealed that it closed in 1998.)

A wide variety of cases were admitted to the Hospital and it provided good training, My Consultant bosses worked hard and provided good supervision.

The post was residential and I lived in the Doctors' Residency.

At the front of the Residency, there were a few parking spaces for medical staff, and these words were on a sign adjacent to the spaces.

However, some of the public abused these spaces. There was actually plenty of free public parking a few hundred metres from the Hospital. Myself and the other doctors got a bit fed up about this. We decided to take action!!

The plan was to have some sticky backed labels, approx. 15cm x 10cm, printed which stated in bold capitals "PLEASE DO NOT ABUSE THE MEDICAL STAFF PARKING".

Accordingly, when our spaces were abused, we put stickers on the offending cars.

Only on the the bodywork, never on lights or windscreens or side windows. Serial offenders (we kept records) had 5 stickers put on their cars. Each one would have taken 5-10 minutes to remove. First time offenders had just one sticker. There were no suspended sentences !! Our actions were very effective !!

Dr. Simon Gibson

THE BURGLAR AND THE OILY DRAINPIPE

On warm nights in the summer, I would leave a window open in my room.

One night, when my then girlfriend was staying, we both woke up to see a burglar in the room. As soon as he realized we were awake, he bolted out of the room, went downstairs and scarpered.

When I had recovered from the shock, I gave chase. He escaped.

What was missing? A bag of frozen peas.

The thief had gained access to my room by climbing up the drainpipe, opened the window fully and climbed in. The real problem was that his hands were covered in anti-theft oil from the drainpipe. And he had wiped his filthy hands on my and my girlfriends clothes.

Needless to say, in the future I always kept my room window closed.

MY RETURN TO COVENTRY

I had accumulated some annual leave. The opportunity to return to the Walsgrave Hospital Coventry, a hospital that held many happy memories, appeared in the jobs section of the BMJ (British Medical Journal). They needed a Locum Consultant Physician and Nephrologist for 4 weeks.

I applied for the job and was awarded the contract. I was to work as a Consultant, where previously I had worked as a SHO (Senior House Officer). Yes I was approaching the top of the greasy pole !!

The Walsgrave is in North Coventry, close to the M6. It covers virtually every specialty and (perhaps most importantly) it has a staff swimming pool. Yes, I was still a swimming obsessive !!!

For the first time, I had my own team. It was ward round day, and we had patients on (as far as I can remember) 3 wards. I led the team onto our first ward. I immediately introduced myself to the Ward Sister. I regarded this as a basic courtesy. See pictures of THE SWANSEA IVORY TOWER HOME OF THE DVLA, after vignette FREE SPEECH? NOT WITH THE D-V-L-AUTOCRACY

I had a simple name badge on my white coat (I had 2 white coats, which I had bought myself. One to wear and the other to wash). My white coats were always scrupulously clean. My badge simply had Dr SP Gibson (I had bought it shortly after qualifying). Today's name badge has job title, photo identity and a barcode. It is mandatory for every doctor in every NHS hospital to prominently display their photo identity when working.

At the end of a ward round there are always small jobs to do: ECG requests, X-ray requests, blood test requests, drug chart re-writes etc etc. The jobs can take 15-30 min, depending on whether or not there is an adequate supply of sticky backed patient identification labels (See vignette Sticky backed... page 20).

As I was leaving the ward, a staff nurse, who had not been on the ward round, came over to me and said "don't forget to come back after the round to sort out the jobs". A little surprised I said the SHO would do that. She replied "but you are the SHO". No I replied, I am the Consultant.

She immediately apologized. I put her at her ease.

Perhaps it was my youthful good looks that had confused her !! (I think not).

WHISTLE IN THE WIND ?? YES. WHISTLE ON THE WARD ?? DEFINETLY NOT !!

My meandering, indecisive career pathway had taken me to Bury District General Hospital (BDGH) to a 6 month post as Senior House Officer (SHO) in Obstetrics and Gynaecology (O+ G).

I was planning to be a GP.

To become a GP, a six month stint (?? sentence) as a SHO in O + G is mandatory.

At BDGH, there were 4 SHOs serving their 6 month sentences in O+ G. This meant that we all worked 09.00 to 17.00, and one night and one weekend in four. Ridiculously long hours.

During 09.00 to 17.00hrs, work was busy but tolerable. It was the 1 in 4 weekend and night rota that could be crushing.

Babies come into the world when they want to and ignore the 9 to 5 convenience hours. And gynaecological problems similarly ignore the 9 to 5 convenience hours.

One night, I was awakened at 02.00hrs. And summoned to the gynaecology ward. A heavily pregnant lady had been admitted with profuse bleeding from her vagina (birth tube).

I arrived on the ward and endeavoured to stem the tide. To do this involved using both of my hands. But I needed help.

The emergency call button was nowhere to be seen. There were 2 midwives at the far end of the ward. Rather than shout help HELP HELP, I whistled to them. The 2 midwifes heard my whistle, and came down the ward.

They immediately gave me a thorough telling off. HOW DARE YOU WHISTLE TO US. WE ARE NOT DOGS. I felt 2 inches tall. In fact I am 6 foot 2 inches tall !! I apologized profusely. In fact, I grovelled.

Nevertheless they recognized the clinical urgency of the situation and helped. The lady was stabilized and then went for an emergency LSCS (Lower Segment Caesarean Section). and a healthy baby boy was delivered.

Later that week I was walking along a corridor at BDGH. Coming in the opposite direction was one of the midwives that had chastised me. She stopped me, and grudgingly told me I had done well for the LSCS lady. She added AND DON'T YOU EVER DARE TO WHISTLE AT A MIDWIFE AGAIN. I apologized again.

The midwives complained to my boss about my "disgraceful conduct". Her response to them was to tell them that she would have a stern word with me.

She did have a quiet word with me. She said that my undoubted whistling talent should not be exhibited at BDGH again !!

MY TRAINING YEAR IN GENERAL PRACTICE

It was early 1986 and I had just failed my first attempt at the MRCP (see vignette "My Exam Failures", page…4). My Senior House Officer rotation in Coventry was coming to an end. I thought I had better head for GP land, as I was worried I would fail my MRCP again and again and again (you were only allowed 4 attempts).

Kenilworth is close to Coventry, and if I did a GP training year there I could return to Coventry for MRCP teaching. Kenilworth is also close to Warwick University, and they had an excellent swimming pool which could be used by the public. At that time in my life I was a swimming obsessive, and liked to swim daily (the Walsgrave Hospital had a staff swimming pool, and Sheffield University had its own pool).

A GP Training Practice in Kenilworth offered me a job as a Trainee, so off to Kenilworth I went. To coincide with the start of my training year, I purchased my first house: a semi-in Tisdale Rise.

Kenilworth is a delightful town in the West Midlands of England. It has its own Castle, which is a little worse for wear thanks to Henry 8th!! See pictures of Kenilworth Castle and Kenilworth High Street. These were downloaded from Bing pictures. It is also close to Warwick Castle.

There were 4 Partners in the Practice, and I made 5.

I saw a wide variety of patients with a wide variety of conditions. It was interesting and enjoyable. I was part of the Practice Team. What was not enjoyable was the very long working hours. We provided a 24hr service 7 days a week, including Bank Holidays.

I did my Family Planning Training in Leamington Spa. See picture of Leamington High Street (downloaded from Bing pictures).

PERHAPS THE MOST IMPORTANT FEATURE OF MY GP TRAINING YEAR WAS THAT I RE-SAT MY MRCP AND PASSED. (See vignette My Exam Failures). I could return to Hospital Medicine if I chose. And I did !!

Dr. Simon Gibson

KENILWORTH CASTLE

KENILWORTH HIGH STREET

LEAMINGTON SPA HIGH ST.

WE MET ACROSS A DIALYSIS MACHINE AND...

Subsequently we fell in love.

My time at East Birmingham Hospital (now renamed Birmingham Heartlands Hospital) was at an end.

I retired to my Kenilworth house and began writing my MD thesis (see vignette "My Exam Failures", page 4) and then the phone rang and it was Prof WJ, Professor of Nephrology at Cardiff University. He invited me to go to Cardiff to work as a Senior Registrar in Nephrology and General Medicine.

Much though I would have liked to get on with my thesis, the mortgage had to be paid, and all the other household bills paid.

And so, I loaded up the car and set off for Cardiff.

On the Dialysis Unit there was a pretty Junior Dialysis Sister, Tes. And we started going out together.

The relationship blossomed. I met her parents. And after a few dates, we fell in love.

My career progressed. Following my appointment in Cardiff, I became Senior Registrar in Nephrology and General Medicine in Bristol. From there I was appointed Consultant in Nephrology and General Medicine, Royal Preston Hospital.

Our marriage ceremony took place in Royal Preston Hospital Chapel (with civil ceremony in Preston Registry Office).

Our reception was held in Royal Preston Hospital Staff Restaurant.

And then Tes and I left for our honeymoon in the Dordogne, France.

Our beloved daughter, S, was born on 2.1.98 at Royal Lancaster Infirmary.

JOY

TO SWAB OR NOT TO SWAB?

That was the question.

A young lady (28) was referred to me by her GP as her blood pressure (BP) was abnormally high for someone of her tender years. She was ? a "young hypertensive". A full medical history was taken.

She mentioned that she had a vaginal discharge. I enquired what was the nature of the discharge. Dark brown was the answer.

I organized the necessary BP investigations: USS (ultrasound scan) of adrenal glands, ECG, 24 hr BP monitoring, numerous blood tests, Chest X-ray, 24 hour urine collections for meta-nephrines (adrenal gland screening for phaeochromocytoma) etc. etc.

I also advised her to see her GP about the vaginal discharge and get a swab done.

At that point she turned on me and said with mild irritation that she would probably have to wait 3-4 weeks to see her GP. And she said with more irritation. "You are a doctor ! You do the damn swab".

Somewhat taken aback, I said OK. I explained to her what was involved. She would need to undress below the waist, bring her legs up and let them flop apart but drapes would cover her pelvic area. A chaperone would be present at all times. I would insert a warmed metal speculum into her vagina, do the swabs x 3, and I would perform a pelvic examination. With even more irritation, she responded "Yeah, Yeah, Doc. Just get on with it. I have had it done before.".

The clinic nurse took her into an examination cubicle, and when the patient was undressed, positioned, and draped I joined them and did the swabs and performed a pelvic examination, a PV). During the PV examination, her cervix felt irregular and rough.

Oh God I thought, surely she has not got cervical cancer. One of the 3 swabs was sent to cytology rather than microbiology. I told her of the abnormal findings but did not mention the possibility of cervical cancer. As was my practice, all swab results were copied through to her GP.

Later that day. I was summoned to see the Medical Director, MD, of RPH. I duly attended, and in his office was my senior colleague, Dr RC.

I was asked to account for my actions. The MD (who was a Consultant Obstetrician and Gynaecologist), feared that I had behaved in-appropriately, and if the press heard about my actions it would be bad publicity for RPH.

My face reddened. RC seemed to enjoy my embarrassment. I explained that the young lady had asked me to do the swabs because of the long delays to be seen at her GP surgery. The MD then said "you are not trained to take vaginal swabs and do pelvic examinations"

Dr. Simon Gibson

I replied that I was a fully trained and accredited GP as well as fully trained and accredited Consultant Physician and Nephrologist (kidney specialist). I added that I had my Family Planning Certificate too !!

There is a general rule in medicine that you should not work outside your areas of expertise.

(Pelvic examinations etc. are a necessary but embarrassing part of General Practice)

The MD expressed surprise at the breadth of my qualifications (see below). His fear of adverse publicity for RPH settled. I returned to my normal duties.

36 hours later, I had an urgent phone call from cytology. Cervical cancer cells had been seen in the young lady's swab.

I immediately referred her to the gynaecology department using the "2 week cancer wait rule". I was a little tempted to refer her to the MD of RPH, and give him some real work, instead of his paper work !!

Three days later, one of RPH's gynaecologists with an interest in oncology (cancer treatment) phoned me and confirmed that the young lady did indeed have cervical cancer. He commended my actions.

Fortunately, no similar case came my way, and I never again performed a PV pelvic examination at RPH.

The following week my clinic nurse said she was impressed with me warming the the metal speculum before inserting it into the young lady's vagina. I told her that a female GP, with whom I had worked with in Birmingham, had suggested this was a kindness. And since then I have always put the sterile packaged speculum on a radiator for a few minutes before use. Of course with a plastic speculum, pre-warming is not necessary. So I am told !!

And what of the young lady? Sadly tests revealed that she had advanced cervical cancer, and surgery was no longer possible. She received chemo-therapy and radiotherapy. I took comfort from knowing that standards of care at RPH are exemplary.

There had been no time to give her a medical examination (auscultation of her heart and lungs, check peripheral pulses etc.). But that could be done at a later date.

In medicine, as in life, you have to prioritise.

Dr SP Gibson BA MB ChB MA MRCP FPCert T(GP) MD FRCP

MALIGNANT DIABETES—THE CASE OF CB

Reader Beware. This vignette may upset you.

Chloe had:

1. A wonderfully supportive family
2. The NHS---always available 24/7, free at the point of delivery, and no questions asked about health insurance etc.

She was a young diabetic who grew tired of the struggle to live. And in her 36th year, decided the struggle was too much.

And she passed, in her mother's arms surrounded by love and beautiful flowers. She loved flowers. She loved life. but the struggle to live was too great.

She went to the Crematorium in a cardboard coffin. Her ashes spread in the green fields she loved.

A young life destroyed by malignant diabetes. Her limbs ischaemic. A toe fell off, her blood vessels wrecked by malignant diabetes. Nearly blind, cataracts and diabetic retinopathy too. Her kidneys surviving, but only just. Acute dialysis she needed a few times when keto-acidosis attacked. Infections too, which made everything worse... Sometimes chest, and sometimes bladder and kidneys too.

Her beautiful mind preserved. Her body not. Full of rot. All due to malignant diabetes. Not her fault. Nobody's fault.

How did I become involved with Chloe? She lived in Lancaster and I was the Renal Consultant who covered Lancaster (and Kendal and Barrow). In fact Chloe lived about 1.5 miles from my house. And in the final week of her life, I called daily at her home. If she had changed her mind I would have admitted her to Royal Preston Hospital stat. Her mother always answered the door and said that Chloe was resting. The house was full of beautiful flowers and beautiful sounds.

And Chloe passed in her mother's arms. Peace at last. She will have sped through the Pearly Gates. No time in Purgatory. Not a second. To eternal life, without malignant diabetes.

RIP Chloe.

I will never forget you. Never. Never.

FUNERAL
TUESDAY 14 MARCH 2000
11:30 am
LANCASTER & MORECAMBE
CREMATORIUM
TORRISHHOLME, LANCASTER.
Chloe wished that her funeral be an
abundance of colour, fight, & flowers and
that while we mourn her death, we also
celebrate her life, her style and her presence.

CELEBRATION
1:30 PM – 5:00 PM FRIENDS
MEETING HOUSE
(Near BR Station) LANCASTER
Where we will share memories,
music, food and much more

As a tribute to Chloe can I ask that
you don't wear mourning clothes.
Cut flowers only (Parry's
Florists – 01524 66410)
to:
Preston Ireland ^ Bowker, 206 Queen
Street, Lancaster (01524 64023)
Donations to Chloe Bently Renal Fund.

CHLOE BENTLY
1964 – 2000
6 march 2000

Chloe died peacefully in my
arms on Monday morning.
Her week at home was everything anyone
could wish for her. The house filled with
love, laughter, friendship, messages of
good will and flowers, flowers, flowers!
She said it was perfect. My thanks to you all.

love

Radhe

Q. KEER VILLAS
CARNFORTH
LANCS LA5 9EY

STICKY BACKED (SELF ADHESIVE) PATIENT IDENTIFICATION LABELS

These were one of my minor obsessions as a Consultant Nephrologist (my secretaries, outpatient nurses and ward clerks might describe it as a major obsession !!).

Why ??

1. They saved time. To get a blood test done, an X-Ray, a cardiac echo, a CT scan, an MIRI scan, an ECG, spirometry etc etc etc etc required the appropriate departmental form to be filled in. These forms all required patient demographics: age, sex, date of birth, hospital number, NHS number, address, etc. Category of urgency (routine or urgent) had to be given. An identification label had much of this information. And could be rapidly attached to the form.
2. They reduced tedium. You try filling in the 7-10 forms which every patient needed at a renal out-patient clinic.
3. They improved clinic efficiency.
4. Their absence possibly made me just a very little bit irritated !!
5. They were hugely useful aide memoire. If I saw a patient in clinic or on the ward who needed some further action, I would pop an address label in my shirt top pocket to remind me. If my shirt had no top pocket, I would put the label in my wallet !! Often I would have 5-10 labels either in my top pocket or wallet.

EVEN WHEN THE SYSTEM DOES EVERYTHING RIGHT...

My involvement with this courageous lady was over a 5 year period. She came under my care because she lived in Kendal. I was the Renal (kidney) Consultant for Kendal.

A tragic case of premature death.

As far as I can recall, the timeline of events was:

1. Mother of two, Family home in Kendal.
2. Relocated to USA because of husband's work.
3. Ovarian cancer diagnosed.
4. Chemotherapy.
5. Radiotherapy.
6. Returned to family home in Kendal.
7. End stage renal failure diagnosed.
8. Dialysis (artificial kidney support) commenced.
9. Ovarian cancer recurred.
10. Dialysis continued.
11. More chemotherapy.
12. Dialysis continued.
13. Disagreement with Oncologist (cancer specialist).
14. Transferred to different Oncologist.
15. Dialysis continued.
16. More chemotherapy.
17. Dialysis continued.
18. Ovarian cancer recurred.
19. Decided against more chemotherapy (her choice).
20. Dialysis continued.
21. Death from disseminated ovarian cancer at age 52.

I will never forget this courageous lady. It was my policy that such individuals afflicted by a nasty cancer and renal failure, should not die of renal failure, ie. should not be denied dialysis.

I remember visiting her on Christmas Day when she was an in-patient at Royal Lancaster Infirmary. And I took my 2 year old daughter with me.

She was surprised and delighted to see us both.

The following Christmas she gave me a present. A bronze of Hippocrates, regarded as the Father of Medicine. See picture of him in action.

WE TRIED AND TRIED BUT COULD NOT SAVE HER

A lady in her early 50s had been admitted to Furness (Barrow) General Hospital.

Seemingly she had a nasty urinary tract infection, but her renal function was deteriorating rapidly. Imaging of her urinary tract was unremarkable.

An urgent renal consultation was requested, and as I was going to Barrow the next day, agreed to see her.

When my morning clinic finished, I went to see her on her admitting ward. She was clearly unwell, with laboured breathing, and sub optimal pulse oximetry. Her urinary tract infection was responding to antibiotics.

But her renal function was continuing to deteriorate.

My suspicion was that she had a vasculitis, and urgently requested numerous highly specialized blood tests.

I arranged for her immediate transfer to Royal Preston Hospital (her clinical condition was safe for travel).

I returned to the Out-Patient Department to start my afternoon clinic.

When I went to see her the next-day I found her on the ITU. Her breathing had deteriorated to such an extent that she needed ventilation, and her renal function had fallen so much that she needed dialysis.

The results of the specialised blood tests confirmed my suspicions. She had an ANCA+ve vasculitis.

After 2 weeks on ITU she was deemed to be fit to go to the renal ward. She was now dialysis dependant.

Sadly her condition replased even thought her vasculitis was responding to potent immunosuppression.

After much discussion with the Director of Intensive Care, we reached a joint decision that a return to the ITU would be futile.

She remained on the renal ward receiving full care, but not including a return to ITU.

Unfortunately her condition continued to deteriorate and she passed.

RIP a lady that in-spite of our best endeavours, we could not save.

For more information about vasculitis please look on internet.

DR X

I have to tread carefully here. This vignette involves criticism of a former colleague. But nobody is above scrutiny. I have thought for 6 months or so about the contents of this vignette.

But I owe it to the patients and their families that he let down in the last 5 years of his professional life.

Terms and descriptions will be deliberately vague and hopefully obscure. But the underlying content will be 100% accurate.

One of the reasons I retired five years early, was to escape from his manipulative bullying. I was able to do this with no loss of pension due to a wonderful investment I had made as a House Officer. I had bought 5 "Added Years of Pension Right". This was very expensive, but I paid for them by monthly deduction from salary over 10 years. It is no longer possible to buy Added Years.

Even though I am retired, it rankles that the behaviour of Dr X has escaped accurate appraisal, and public exposure. He managed to project an image of being a "wonderful, very hard working, successful Consultant". But in the last 5 years of his working life he became selfish and arrogant.

And he lined his own pockets at the expense of patients, and their families. And at my expense (mentally). It became so bad that I considered resigning my Consultancy and moving to escape the bully. But that would have caused massive disruption to my family, in particular disruption to my daughter's education as she was settled at the local grammar school.

There are clear guidelines as to where patients with kidney impairment/failure should be looked after. I fully agreed with them, as it was what I would wish for myself and my family.

Dr X chose to ignore these guidelines, so that he could free up time to get "brownie points". And lots of brownie points means a massive increase in pension. The official term for brownie points is merit points

I suspect that Dr X's pension is 5x mine. I can live comfortably on my basic NHS pension plus my state pension. But I have no interest in lavish luxury cruises every 3 months and expensive meals out every other night, and a new luxury car every year etc.

The National Guidelines, the Renal Association Guidelines, and the Local guidelines all say that:

Patients should be seen as close to their home as possible.

A first OPD (Out Patient Department) assessment should usually be done in the OPD close to the patients home.

I agreed with all of this, as it would be what I would want for myself and my family. And it happened in my catchment area (At PH, the arrangements were that we all had central responsibilities at PH , and each had a separate catchment area to look after. Thus Dr SL had LE , Dr X had FBF, and I had BM.)

But Dr X ignored most of his new patient responsibilities in FBF.

And many new elderly, often disabled patients ended up coming to my clinic at PH, travelling past two of Dr X's OPD clinics in FBF.

I went to see the Medical Director of PH, (The Medical Director is the most senior Doctor in a hospital) to try and get him to stop Dr X's surprising behaviour. But I got nowhere, as Dr X had friends in very high places. I did not, as I was patient focused, and not self- focused.

So I did the only thing I could do, retire early. And I was totally worn out, burnt out and utterly depressed.

Where is Dr X now? Probably far away in an overseas tax haven, counting his loot.

Please also read the vignette: THE PEARLY GATES PURGATORY JUGGEMENT DAY HEAVEN page 61.

MY PATIENTS WHO WERE MY NEIGHBOURS

Surprisingly there were two, N1 and N2.

What is the statistical probability of this ?? I have no idea. Perhaps I should consult Prof PD, another one of my patients, who is Distinguished Professor of Medical Statistics at Lancaster University.

N1

His house was about 500m from mine. He was a renal transplant recipient. Previously, he had been on Home Haemodialysis (HHD). This means he had a blood dialysis machine at his home and dialysed himself with the assistance of his wife. It is a very cost effective variety of dialysis (see vignette Hey Big Spender, page 60). He was pleased when my Lancaster Clinic started as more of his management could be done closer to his home.

His transplant function was very slowly declining, as can happen. But he was decades away from needing a second transplant. Most transplant recipients regard EVERY DAY OFF DIALYSIS AS A GOOD DAY.

All was going well until he developed a chest infection, which you or I would throw off in a day or so. Not him. Within 3 weeks of the start of symptoms he was dead. RIP N1. This was despite of the best efforts of the Intensive Care Unit at Royal Lancaster Infirmary.

Why had this happened ?? BECAUSE HE WAS IMMUNOSUPPRESSED. To keep a transplant healthy, and avoid rejection, potent immunosuppressive drugs are required. IF YOU HAVE AN IDENTICAL TWIN, ALWAYS STAY FRIENDS. And some time you may need a kidney or a piece of liver from him/her. Far less immunosuppression is required.

Cynics might say that when a dialysis patient is transplanted, you just replace one set of problems with another. I am definitely not of this persuasion. And transplantation was always the goal for my patients.

Sadly, if your kidneys fail, you will need lifelong health supervision. Be thankful we have the NHS.

RIP N1

N2

This is a lady who came under my care in her mid 30s as she lived in Lancaster. I say "my care," but it is always a team effort. The Consultant, after discussions with the team, invariably makes the final decision. She was a district nurse. Her house was about 750m from my house. The origin of her kidney failure was thought to be recurrent urinary tract infections (UTIs). She was under regular follow up. There was a sudden deterioration in her kidney function. Possibly she had contracted another UTI. She was immediately over-booked onto my next Preston Clinic (which was the next day). The dialysis education team was alerted, and the Transplant Sister. And yes I asked my Preston secretary to make sure there was a double dose of sticky backed (self adhesive) patient identification labels in her Preston notes See vignette "sticky backed self-adhesive patient identification labels". All her parameters were repeated. Lots of sticky labels were used. Her husband was with her. Discussions about dialysis and transplantation followed.

She had opted for peritoneal dialysis. She needed urgent insertion of a peritoneal dialysis catheter. As usual there were no beds available. But after much pleading and begging I managed to secure a bed on a neurosurgical ward. Her catheter was inserted the next day, and she began her dialysis life.

But she was not on dialysis long. Why ?? HER HUSBAND DONATED ONE OF HIS KIDNEYS TO HER.

A LEGACY OF SPINA BIFIDA

Spina bifida is a malformation of the vertebrae of the spine. That exposes the spinal nerve system.

It is fairly common (> 20,000 cases per year in the UK). It can cause severe disability in those those affected.

For more information, put Spina Bifida into an internet search engine.

I first learnt about this condition when I was a medical student at Sheffield University Medical School. I had a 4 week attachment to Prof L and his team. Prof L was a world authority on the condition. He expected his students to memorize every detail of their allocated patient down to the last WBC (White Blood Cell) in their urine. My memory was not that good then. And it is even worse now! If you made mistake when presenting your case to the Prof, he was not a happy man, and he expressed himself accordingly. Happy Days ?? No, but I did learn a lot about spine bifida.

This vignette describes the case of LT with spina bifida. She came under my care because she lived in Lancaster, and I was the Nephrologist (kidney specialist) for Lancaster (and Kendal and Barrow).

The condition had rendered her wheel-chair bound, and needing dialysis. Her kidneys had failed because of ?? recurrent urinary tract infections. To satisfy the metabolic needs of her body she required 3x weekly haemodialysis sessions, each one lasting 6 hours. She had these at Royal Preston Hospital, RPH, or occasionally at Kendal Hospital, WGH.

It took about 1hr to travel from her home to the dialysis unit at RPH and 1hr to travel back. In total she lost 3 days a week. And what did she do with the other 4 days ?

Three were spent in part time employment. It is rare for those on haemodialysis to do anything on their dialysis free days. She had the Sabbath off.

When I saw her on the dialysis unit she was always reading or planning social activities for herself and other similarly disabled. They would go the cinema, the theatre, stately homes etc etc. In fact, her social life was better than mine !!

In spite of her many difficulties, she was always polite and courteous and never complained about the life that fate had dealt her.

She was helped at all times by her devoted parents.

Dr. Simon Gibson

It was about 5 years into my retirement when by chance I met her father in Asda Lancaster car park. I enquired after LT. To my surprise, her father told me she died about 18 months ago, from disseminated bladder cancer. How old was she when she passed? In her 40s.

We should all count our blessings. There are always people worse off than ourselves.

Let the life of LT be an inspiration to us all!

RIP LT. I will never forget you.

PROVERBS   10:6
PSALM   128:2

NO SALT OR LO-SALT. THAT WAS THE QUESTION

A vignette from my time as Senior Registrar in Renal Medicine in Bristol. (Bristol Royal Infirmary and Southmead Hospital).

I was resident in Wales when staying with my girlfriend in Wales (who was to become my wife, and mother of our beloved daughter S), and had a room in a shared NHS house when on call in Bristol.

Travel between Newport and Bristol was easy. The magnificent Severn Bridge (see figure, downloaded via Bing) had fixed all the previous congestion issues.

I was seeing a man in clinic with high blood pressure and moderate renal failure, and a disproportionately high serum potassium (K+).

And if serum potassium reaches 7, CARDIAC ARREST OCCURS.

I listened to his heart with my trusty stethoscope to check if there was pericarditis (inflammation of the outer layer of the heart). If severe, CARDIAC ARREST OCCURS.

I asked him about his salt intake. No problem Doc he said, I have switched to LoSalt for cooking and as a condiment.

I TOLD HIM TO IMMEDIATELY STOP TAKING Lo-Salt.

Why? Because LoSalt is stuffed with potassium. KCl has been substituted for NaCl (sodium chloride).

With cessation of LoSalt, his serum potassium subsided, and returned to a level appropriate to his degree of renal failure.

Attention to every detail of a renal patient's life is essential, or needless premature death occurs.

And I practice what I preach.

SEVERN BRIDGE

FESTIVE FUN

At Royal Preston Hospital, as Christmas Day approached, I would abandon my usual discreet shirt tie in favour of my bright red "Santa Tie" (see photo).

And it was a "Musical Tie". If I pressed on Santa, festive music emerged!!

Thus renal staff (Dialysis Unit and Renal Ward) were treated to Festive Fun.

And my Santa Tie travelled with me to the other hospitals that I worked at: Royal Lancaster Infirmary, Kendal Hospital and Barrow Hospital.

The journeys were made by car and not by sleigh!!

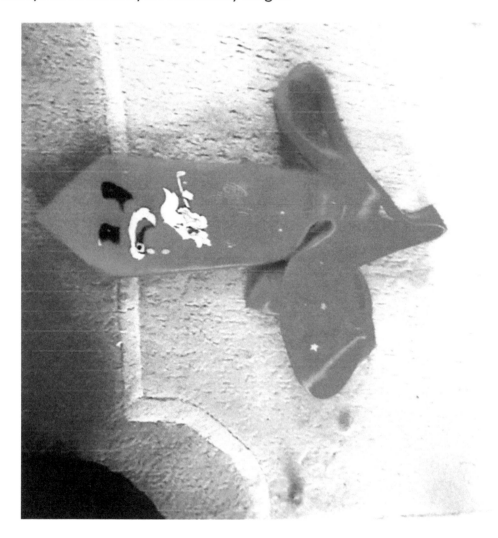

Dr. Simon Gibson

SEDBERGH

Sedbergh is a small town and civil parish in Cumbria. It lies roughly 10 miles east of Kendal and 28 miles north of Lancaster. It is Englands' Official "Book Town". There are numerous independent booksellers located in the town. Glorious open countryside surrounds the town. See picture of Sedbergh High Street (down loaded from Bing pictures).

A resident of Sedbergh needed long term renal follow-up because she had Polycystic Kidney Disease (PKD). I saw her in my Kendal Clinic at Westmorland General Hospital (WGH).

PKD is an interesting condition. It is inherited. Cysts develop in the kidneys, and to a lesser extent in the liver, and in females the ovaries. Typically those with PKD might have elevated blood pressure (BP), abdominal (tummy) discomfort, and slowly deteriorating kidney function.

Whenever she came to clinic, I would (deliberately) mis-pronounce Sedbergh. Locals say Sedba. I would say Sedburga or Sedburger. She would laugh and correct me. It was a bit of fun.

Thankfully, her PKD caused her few problems. Her elevated BP was easily controlled, her cysts were increasing in size slowly, and her kidney function was deteriorating slowly.

Sometimes laughter is the best medicine !!

SLEEP

Shortly after I retired, I was walking from my home into Lancaster. The route I followed took me past my then GP's house. And by chance she was outside working in the garden (it was a Sunday).

As I went past, she greeted me and said "Simon I hear you have retired. Congratulations!" She asked me what I was planning to do in retirement? I replied: Sleep. Good she said, but what are you going to do when you wake-up? I replied: go back to sleep.

I was going to reduce the massive sleep deficit that had accrued from all the nights on-call.

Patients don't stop being ill at 17.00 or 18.00, and new admissions arrive at any time of day. All require careful assessment and then active management as appropriate.

In kidney medicine, it is always a Consultant decision that dialysis should start in a new arrival with advanced kidney failure. His or her decision commits the NHS to spending very large sums of money on continuing dialysis until the patient is transplanted or dies. See vignette "Hey Big Spender" page 60. And that means kidney specialists are often called into hospitals with Renal Units, at night and at weekends. And that means disturbed sleep.

My then GP was hard working, completely dedicated to her role as a family doctor, highly skilled and had a delightful personality. But she was a cigarette smoker, and despite her best endeavours could not quit the habit.

And she died of a smoking related cancer in her early 50s.

When later and my own health declined, my GP was highly skilled, and made an accurate assessment of my condition, ordered the required head scans which revealed my underlying problem.

And he is a non-smoker.

Dr. Simon Gibson

THE ARTERIO-VENOUS FISTULA (THE ROUTE TO HEAVEN ??)

If you have chronic kidney disease (CKD) and have opted for haemodialysis (HD), you will need to have special access created to your veins. UK guidelines recommend that you have an "arterio-venous fistula" (AVF) created.

A highly skilled vascular surgeon joins a vein onto an artery, usually in the arm. This creates a large robust blood vessel that can have dialysis needles regularly inserted for haemodialysis.

Haemodialysis involves blood leaving the body, entering the dialysis machine to be cleansed in an artificial kidney, and then returned to the body. To achieve rapid cleaning of the blood, large volumes leave via the fistula, and the blood is pumped through the artificial kidney and then returned to the body.

Once created, the fistula may take 3-6 months to mature before it is ready for use, so forward planning is essential. For those presenting in renal failure without a fistula, there are alternative means of taking blood out of the body and into the dialysis machine.

But the route to heaven can be fraught with problems:

1. The fistula may clot. This is an absolute emergency and de-clotting services are available 24/7.
2. Too much arterial blood going into the fistula can starve the hand and fingers of blood: a Steal Syndrome develops. Thankfully it happens in less than 10%.
3. The wound at the site of fistula creation can become infected. This warrants immediate intravenous antibiotics.
4. The fistula arm may become swollen.
5. The fistula itself can become infected. This again warrants immediate potent antibiotics or the fistula may clot.

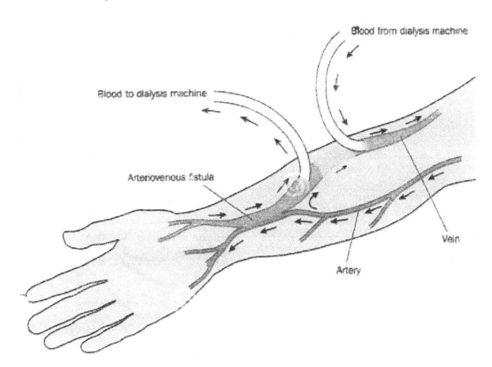

HAEMODIALYSIS MACHINE WITH PATIENT "PLUMBED" IN

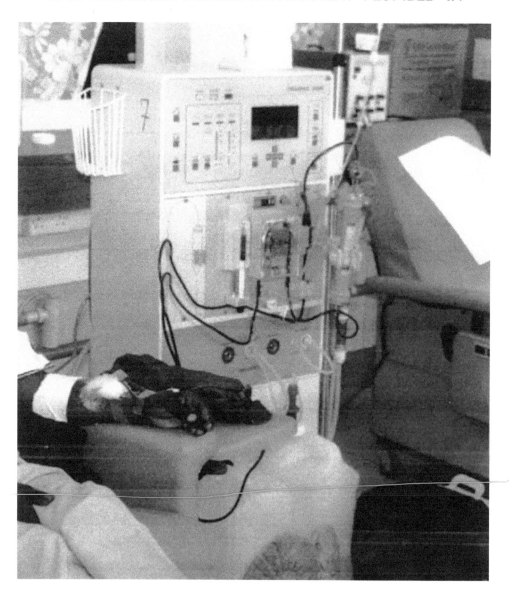

A TEMPORARY DUAL LUMEN CATHETER (ARTERY + VENOUS SIDES) FOR EMERGENCY VASCULAR ACCESS

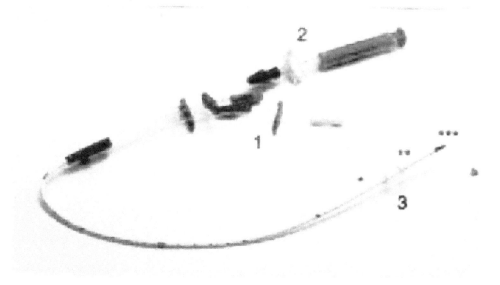

RENAL FAILURE AND MENTAL ILLNESS

Coping with mental illness is difficult. But when it is accompanied by kidney problems, difficulties escalate exponentially.

Two patients have lingered in my memory.

1. A schizophrenic on haemodialysis. He was in his early 20s. The cause of his renal failure had not been established. He had needed dialysis since the age of 18. He was receiving a cocktail of antipsychotic drugs to control his schizophrenia.

    His attendance for dialysis was erratic. Sometimes he would turn up on time, sometimes late and sometimes not at all. He never came to my Outpatient Clinic for formal review. That did not really matter, as I was willing to review him on the Dialysis Unit.

    His attendance seemed to be related to his compliance with taking his antipsychotic medication.

    In a particular week, he did not turn up for dialysis at all. The next week the same happened. The police were contacted. They went round to his flat, made a forcible entry, and found him dead.

    What had gone wrong?? Difficult. Possibly he felt so well on his antipsychotic medication that he thought he could reduce the dosage or stop them. No post-mortem was held.

    RIP I will not forget you.

RENAL FAILURE AND MENTAL ILLNESS CONTD. CASE 2

This was an adolescent girl who was both mentally and physically handicapped. She lived in a care home. She had lost about 60% of her renal function. I saw her in my Kendal Clinic. She was always accompanied by one of the Care Home staff when she attended clinic.

It was always very difficult to get blood samples from her. She simply did not understand the importance of regular monitoring of her kidney function, and would struggle as we attempted to get a blood sample.

Her GP had much greater success. He had known her from an early age and she felt at ease when he was getting the necessary samples. And her GP would always send a copy of the blood results through to my clinic.

Thankfully her kidney function was declining very slowly.

Her GP and I monitored her parameters, and I added any extra medication to ameliorate the effects of her renal deficit.

This joint management continued for about 2 years until the young lady relocated to a different part of to the country so that she could be looked after in a care home more suited to an 18 year old.

Dr. Simon Gibson

ONE KIDNEY TWO KIDNEYS THREE KIDNEYS DIALYSIS TRANSPLANTATION

The majority of us have 2 kidneys. Some only have one. But we all have an "extra" kidney: the lining of the abdomen (tummy).

These facts can be established with a simple ultrasound scan (USS).

While radiologists are the true experts at performing an USS, many nephrologists (myself included) became gifted amateurs.

This was a useful skill to have especially at 02.00hrs or 03.00hrs when an emergency patient was admitted. Within a few minutes you could gain truly vital information: one kidney or two kidneys AND MOST IMPORTANT OF ALL KIDNEY SIZE AND IF THERE WAS A BLOCKAGE IN THE PLUMBING.

If the kidneys were small and shrunken, then sadly the patient was destined for dialysis and renal transplantation.

If there was a plumbing (urinary tract obstruction) problem, then a skilled urologist could fix it. This offered the best chance of kidney recovery.

It was routine for a radiologist to look at the abdominal blood vessels. I did not attempt to do this. Typically an abdominal aortic aneurysm (AAA) might be detected. Indeed there is a UK screening programmed for AAA as skilled surgeons can fix them.

It was vital for every patient to have a formal USS by a radiologist or a sonagrapher (someone who had specialist training in USS). A scan by a gifted amateur was not sufficient. But that could wait to a more civilized hour. I suspect that in Germany, training in US was mandatory for nephrologists. Certainly Prof A W was a skilled sonographer.

In the UK, the maxim that you should not work outside your specialist area applies. See "to swab or not to swab".

It is perfectly possible for someone to be entirely healthy with just one kidney. Often this fact is a chance finding on an USS done for an unrelated reason. But you need to be extra careful if you have one kidney. The Good Lord (or evolution) gave us 2 kidneys for good reasons.

Everybody has a third or (second) kidney. The lining of the abdominal (tummy) cavity, the peritoneum. This can function as a dialysis membrane but it is not very efficient. Those on peritoneal dialysis (PD) usually have to do it 24hrs a day, 7 days a week. But there are variants of the technique. The big weakness of PD is infection.

?? THE CORRECT CHOICE

An 80 year old lady appeared from nowhere with very advanced kidney failure. As I was the duty Consultant, she came under my care ("my care" means "the team" care, as it is always a team effort to help those unfortunate enough to have kidney failure, the Consultant is the leader of the team, and the one who has to make the really big decisions, and the one who bears ultimate responsibility).

She appeared to be of sound mind. The renal education team (highly experienced kidney nurses, social worker) went to see her to discuss dialysis life. Life on dialysis is a very difficult and disciplined existence, but it is life. She was almost certainly too old for a kidney transplant.

She was a "loner". Husband had passed, no brothers or sisters, no children, and seemingly no friends as nobody came to visit her.

She chose not to have life extending dialysis.

A few days later, her case was discussed at our weekly lunchtime multi-disciplinary team meeting. She was occupying a bed on the renal ward, a bed that would usually be occupied by a dialysis patient with an intercurrent problem. The majority view was that she should immediately be transferred to a hospice for terminal care. I refused, and as I was her Consultant, could not be overruled.

I had to provide an explanation for my decision. In my judgment, she had at best only a week or so to live. She had become familiar with the renal nurses, cleaners, porters, and doctors in training with me, on the renal ward. In effect we had become her family.

She passed a week later, in familiar surroundings, with some of her new family at her bedside.

Was my decision correct ?? That is for others to judge. But my conscience remains clear.

RIP a courageous lady, who made her own choice.

I will never forget you.

Dr. Simon Gibson

VERBAL ABUSE THREATENED PHYSICAL ABUSE

Yes, you can get it all as a Consultant Nephrologist.

It was early one Monday morning and I was en-route to FGH. I had just left the dreaded A590 (locally known as the "Road of Death" due to the high number of accidents that occurred along it).

My mobile phone rang, and I pulled off the road to answer it. It was R, the sister in charge of the satellite Dialysis Unit at WGH. There was a plumbing problem on the Dialysis Unit, and no dialysis was possible that day, until the plumbing problem was fixed. R had spoken to C, the sister in charge of the main unit at RPH. The WGH dialysis patients would dialyse in the evening at RPH or the next day. The arrangements were good in the circumstances, and I agreed with the plan. I resumed my journey to FGH.

After a further 5 miles or so, the mobile rang again. I again pulled off the road again to answer it. The caller was the husband of one of the Kendal dialysis patients (I don't know how he obtained the number of my mobile). He was incandescent with rage. He cursed me, swore at me etc. and threatened me with physical violence.

Why ?? Apparently he and his wife had planned a visit to some tourist attraction for her non dialysis day, but that would have to be cancelled as she would have to dialyse at RPH on that day. He thought that I was responsible for the plumbing on the dialysis unit at WGH. After all, I was the Consultant in charge of the unit.

The next time I saw this patient (she had Polycystic Kidney Disease) I informed her that I would never speak to her husband again unless he apologized for his disgraceful behaviour. He never did, and so I never spoke to him again.

And what happened to this patient? I saw her on a number of occasions and she repeatedly apologized for her husband's behaviour. Within 2 years she was fortunate to receive a kidney transplant.

And did I arrive late for my clinic at FGH ?? No. Why ?? Because I always allowed extra travelling time for unseen problems (usually traffic congestion etc…). But there was no time for my pre-clinic cup of coffee and chat with the nurses !!

A YOUNG MAN WHOSE LIFE WOULD NEVER BE THE SAME AGAIN

A 17 year old young man had presented to BH Casualty Department feeling tired, nauseous, worn out, short of breath, debilitated etc. etc. All the usual investigations were done, and five minutes after the results were reviewed, I received a phone call. I was at PH in my office at the time.

I asked what the young man's serum potassium (K+) was. As it was safe for travel, I said he should be immediately transferred to the Renal Ward at PH. The caller asked if there would be a bed available. I said that was my problem. (Emergency transfers had to have a clearly defined destination, so the ambulance staff knew where to take the patient).

I immediately phoned the Renal Ward and fortunately a bed was available. Someone was being discharged that morning. The young man was booked into that bed.

Upon arrival on the Renal Ward, he was examined and a wide variety of additional tests were requested, including an emergency USS of his urinary system.

About 30 min. later, I received a phone call from one of my radiologist colleagues. The young man's kidneys were small and shrunken and there was no obstruction (plumbing problem). Sadly this meant that the young man's kidneys were irreversibly damaged and his future would be dialysis then transplantation.

I went to the Renal Ward to give the bad news to the young man. As he was 17, his parents/guardian did not need to be involved (he had reached the age of "medical responsibility"). Before speaking to the young man, I explained to the Ward Sister (who I had known for over a decade) what the situation was. She and a few renal nurses and a student nurse came with me to the bedside.

As was my long established policy, I told the (perhaps brutal) truth to young man that his kidneys were small, shrunken and irreversibly damaged. The student nurse left the bedside. I immediately told the young man that there was lots the system could do to restore him to good health: dialysis, transplantation etc., and the Dialysis Education Team would see him later that day. BUT HIS LIFE WOULD NEVER BE THE SAME AGAIN.

As I was leaving the ward, the young student nurse who had left the bedside, came over to me and said "you were brutal with that young patient". Somewhat taken aback, I said that that if she had remained at the bedside, she would have heard me immediately tell him the good news: about dialysis and transplantation. Her eyes looked upward and she walked off.

Later that week, I related the incident to the Ward Sister. I said that the young student nurse had been a little impertinent to criticize a very senior Nephrologist, who was shortly to retire after a working lifetime of service to the NHS (I never did private work). She agreed. And said she would have a "quiet word" with the young student nurse. My memory reached back to my time as an SHO in Obstetrics and Gynaecology (see vignette "WHISTLE ON THE WIND ?? YES WHISTLE ON THE WARD ?? DEFINETLY NOT !!," page 11).

Dr. Simon Gibson

THE CADBURY'S CREAM EGG SAGA

This began when I was renal registrar then renal research registrar at East Birmingham Hospital (EBH) approximately 1988-1992.

One Easter Sunday I was working on the Haemodialysis Unit at EBH, and one of the dialysis nurses gave me and his colleagues a Cadbury's Cream Egg. I thought what a kind thing to do. I knew my salary exceeded his, so I offered to take over responsibility for future cream egg deliveries. I expanded the cream egg service to staff on the renal ward.

Subsequently, I took the tradition to the other hospitals that I worked at.(see The Meanderings page 2). As Consultant Nephrologist, I provided services at Preston (RPH), Lancaster (RLI), Kendal (Westmoreland General Hospital, WGH) and Barrow (Furness General Hospital, FGH) The number of Cream Eggs required at Easter was significant (>100)!!

I had to have a repeat CT scan of my head on 24.8.20 at RPH, and afterwards I visited the Haemodialysis Unit. The first person I saw was Christina, the Senior Dialysis Sister. A delightful lady who I had not had any contact with for 7 years. She enquired as to why I was at RPH. I told here that I had been for a CT scan of my head. Why she asked ? I told her about the change in my health, requiring neurosurgery and VP shunt insertion. She immediately stopped what she was doing and came and gave me a big hug. Neither she nor I knew if this was allowed under current corona /covid 19 rules. But I was wearing a face mask !!

As I was leaving the Unit another nurse looked at me and unable to remember my name, said hello Cream Egg Consultant.

Small acts of kindness linger in memories, even when names are forgotten. I suppose my Cream Egg gifts were an early personal form of the "Thursday Clap".

Did my successor continue with the tradition ??

No comment.

A CADBURY'S CRÈME EGG

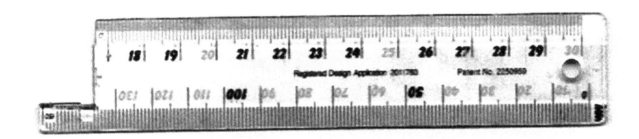

DO NOT EVER UNDERESTIMATE THE DETERMINATION OF PATIENTS TO SEEK JUSTICE

I first met Mr. D shortly after my Kendal Clinic commenced (March 1996).

He was clearly a highly intelligent man. He had founded a very successful company. Sadly he had contracted AIDS (HIV infection with clinical sequelae). The cause of this was unknown. It was not my concern.

He had fairly advanced kidney disease (approx. 80% loss of function).

Why ??

1. Possibly incorrect HIV treatment dosage.
2. Possible he might have HIVAN. An inflammation of the kidneys associated with HIV infection.
3. Possibly unknown factors.

The precise diagnosis of his chronic renal failure did not matter. It was his future management that was critical.

Sadly MBHA (Morecambe Bay Health Authority) did not have the sense (or money) to employ a fully accredited HIV Consultant. Instead they imposed HIV care on an already overworked Chest Consultant. He did his very best but possibly his management of Mr. D may have possibly been sub-optimal at times.

Mr. D sued MBHA and won. And received massive damages with costs, estimated to be £200,000.

With careful, meticulous management his kidney function improved, and when I retired, his deficit was down to 40%.

SO MACHO MANAGERS BEWARE.

THE TRAGIC DEATH OF A YOUNG DOCTOR (TDYD1)

In my early professional life, I shared a hospital flat with M and TDYD1. M and I came through Medical School together. He had a long-term girlfriend, C. My girlfriend then was S. Both C and S were nurses.

M and I did not know TDYD1 well. He had simply just been allocated to the same flat in the Doctor's Residence at H as us.

M, C, S, and I would socialize together when we had time off. We would go out together for walks and visits to the glorious countryside close to H. Sadly S invariably worked a different rota to C, so rarely joined our "bubble" physically, but always did over the phone.

We rarely visited restaurants as C was a brilliant cook. M was also a good cook And what of my cooking skills then ?? No comment.

About 2 months into our appointments at H, M and I returned to the Doctor's Residency at H after a very enjoyable weekend off. There was no sign of TDYD1. We thought nothing of this. We assumed that TDYD1 had his own social circle (bubble).

2 days passed, and there was still no sign of TDYD1. Then we heard on the local media that TDYD1 had been found dead in a park close to H.

He had taken a massive overdose of anti-depressant (AD) tablets.

Neither M nor I nor the ward staff on the ward that TDYD1 worked knew about his depression. He showed no evidence of it on the rare brief occasions we saw him in the flat. TDYD1 always kept his ADs hidden in his locked room.

But M and I were "Doctors". Why had we not noticed TDYD1's tragic descent into the total blackness of severe depression? Answer: We rarely saw him because of the ridiculously long hours we worked (see vignette A MARS BAR AN HOUR). And Drs then were not allowed to admit to their mental health issues.

There was no counselling for M and I following the death of our colleague. We simply had to "man-up" and get on with our jobs. After all, we were Doctors.

RIP TDYD1

I will never forget you.

THE TRAGIC DEATH OF ANOTHER YOUNG DOCTOR (TDYD2)

This sad vignette is from the early part of my Consultancy in General and Renal Medicine.

For the general medical work, a young newly qualified young doctor joined the team to help and gain more experience. Such doctors are known as House Officers.

TDYD2 was full of enthusiasm, courtesy and dedication and very keen to learn from me and other members of the team. He never minded working late (ie. beyond the end of his shift) if the clinical situation warranted it.

All went well for 2-3 months, then TDYD2 did not show up for work. After another day away, his room in the Doctor's Residency was opened by the Caretaker of the building, and TDYD 2 was found dead.

What had happened ?? Post-mortem showed an intracranial bleed from a ruptured intracranial aneurysm (ICA). An aneurysm is a weakness in a blood vessel which may enlarge and rupture. Such occurrences are thankfully rare (< 20.000 cases per year in the UK).

I was given compassionate leave to attend the funeral.

There is some genetic component to ICAs. All members of TDYD2's family were screened for an ICA, and none were found. There is a genetic association between Polycystic Kidney Disease (PKD) and ICAs.

For more information put intracranial aneurysm into an internet search engine or see your GP (if you can get an appointment).

RIP TDYD2

I will never forget you.

There was no TDYD3

ANOTHER MACHO MANAGER ??

This vignette dates from my time as Medical Registrar at East Birmingham Hospital (now renamed Birmingham Heartlands Hospital).

As part of my duties, I was obliged to lead an early morning Ward Round (08.00) on the Acute Medical Unit (AMU), to review medical patients that had been admitted in the previous 24 hours. This duty followed the on-call rota. On that day I was also the lead clinician for the Cardiac Arrest Team.

One day, just as we were about to start the 08.00 ward round, a cardiac arrest call came through. We immediately raced off to attend the call.

Some 15 minutes later, while we were battling to save the life of a 75 year old man, my radio-pager went off. I asked a nursing colleague to answer it for me. She returned about a minute later saying it was Mr.............asking (demanding) to know where I was and why I had not started the AMU ward round. I asked the nurse to tell him I was busy. AT A CARDIAC ARREST.

I would have liked the nurse to tell Mr........to take a long walk off a short pier, but of course did not.

I wondered if it was the same manager that had tried to mess around with our mid morning drinks in the Out Patients Department. See vignette Mid Morning Coffee or Tea ??, page 59.

HIGH BLOOD PRESSURE ?? HAVE YOU BEEN ADVISED TO REDUCE SALT INTAKE ??

A vignette from my time as Senior Registrar in Renal Medicine in Bristol.

I was seeing a man in his late 50s in clinic with high blood pressure and moderate renal failure, and he had a disproportionately high serum potassium (K+).

And if K+ reaches 7. CARDIAC ARREST CAN OCCUR.

I listened to his heart with my trusty stethoscope to check if there was pericarditis (inflammation of layers of heart). IF SEVERE, CARDIAC ARREST OCCURS.

I asked him about salt intake. No problem Doc he said. I have switched to Low Salt for cooking and as a condiment.

I TOLD HIM TO IMMEDIATELY STOP TAKING LowSalt.

Why? LowSalt IS STUFFED WITH POTASSIUM. KCl has been substituted for NaCl.

Within weeks of him ceasing to use LowSalt, his serum K+ returned to expected levels.

ANOTHER PATIENT WITH RECURRENT URINARY TRACT INFECTIONS (UTIs)

This lady was in her 50s, highly intelligent, and I think was married to a train driver. She experienced a UTI at least monthly, and occasionally weekly. Of course she had her own supply of urine dipstix. She also had mild to moderate renal failure, no doubt related to her UTIs, hence my involvement.

Her condition was managed by herself, her GP, and myself. Her GP was hugely supportive and would always find time for an extra consultation, or would write a prescription for a new antibiotic at short notice.

Why has this lady lingered in my memory? Because she took a great interest in my family. She was always asking how my daughter was getting on at school etc. etc. She was keen to see a photograph of my daughter. On one occasion I obliged, and she was thrilled.

WASTE OF TIME... WASTE OF TREES

One afternoon, my Lancaster secretary phoned me saying she had been contacted by a Garstang GP with an urgent referral.

Garstang is a very attractive market town.

The urgent referral was a 75 year old lady who had been found to have advanced renal failure. As ever I told my secretary she could be over booked onto my next Lancaster Clinic (in 24hrs time) at Royal Lancaster Infirmary (RLI).

And of course I reminded my secretary to make sure the patients notes had a double dose of Sticky Backed (Self Adhesive) Patient Identification Labels at the back of the case notes See vignette on page 20.

There was nothing unusual about the GPs urgent telephone referral. What was unusual was the paper referral which he sent to clinic; it consisted of a single sheet of A4 paper with a few patient demographic details AND A 1cm THICK WAD OF COMPUTER PRINTOUT.

In the referral letter the GP had said full Past Medical History (PMH). Drug History (DH) etc. are in the enclosed computer printout. He obviously expected me to trawl through the 1cm wad of verbiage to find the information that I needed amongst details of the patients hair colour, shoe size, dress size, the phase of the moon when the patient had first registered at the practice etc etc etc etc etc. IT WASTED ABOUT 15 MINUTES OF CLINIC TIME.

Every Consultant out patient clinic is busy, regardless of the specialty. Perhaps this thoughtless GP should attend a few, to remind him of the realities of Hospital Medicine and Surgery.

In fact I condensed the 1cm wad of computer paper into 3 lines as there were only 3 serum creatinine results in the whole wad. Serum creatinine is a surrogate estimate of kidney function.

What did I do with the 1cm wad, which was printed on one side of the paper? I saw no reason why RLI should bear the costs of the confidentially disposing of the paper.

In fact, I asked my secretary to return the wad to the GP with a cryptic note.

WHAT A WASTE OF TIME. WHAT A WASTE OF TREES

I have been a donor to The Woodland Trust for 30 years. I like trees!!!!

THE GOOD - THE BAD - THE VERY VERY UGLY
GOODPASTURE'S SYNDROME

This vignette is from my time as Registrar/Research Registrar at East Birmingham Hospital EBH (now renamed Birmingham Heartlands Hospital).

A previously fit young man (MJ) saw his GP as he was feeling tired and utterly debilitated. Blood tests revealed anemia and advanced renal (kidney) failure. He was immediately admitted to the renal ward for further investigations. Scans and specialized blood tests followed, and these revealed that he had Goodpasture's Syndrome, also known as Anti-GBM disease (GBM is an abbreviation of Glomerular Basement Membrane). Please put these terms into an internet search engine.

Goodpasture's Syndrome is rare and a GP may not see a case of it in the whole of his/her working life. It is a very, very ugly, condition, and can cause rapidly progressive kidney failure, and bleeding into the lungs (pulmonary haemorrhage). Both can result in premature death.

Time is of the essence in managing Anti-GBM disease. Prompt diagnosis and treatment is essential, if premature death is to be avoided.

Sadly MJ progressed to needing dialysis (artificial kidney support, please see vignette "The Arterio-Venous Fistula (The Route To Heaven ??), page 35. This meant he had to be plumbed into a kidney machine for 3x8 hour sessions weekly.

He was hopelessly blood transfusion dependent and needed 2-4 units weekly. These were given on dialysis.

He became unemployed. Then came rHuEpo, recombinant Human Erythropoitin, EPO. MJ was the first recipient in the West Midlands to receive this novel treatment. I was the Research Registrar involved in running the trial of EPO. See pictures downloaded via Bing.

EPO is usually given into a vein but can also be given sub cutaneously, but stings a little if given this way.

His blood count gradually increased. Within 4-6 months he was no longer blood transfusion dependent. This is very important if a kidney transplant is contemplated (less antibody sensitisation). His awful tiredness and malaise had been abolished. He found a part-time job (on non-dialysis days), and he once again became a tax payer.

Monitoring of EPO therapy requires regular haemoglobin checks and meticulous blood pressure checking if hypertensive encephalopathy (please look up this condition on the internet) is to be avoided.

EPO is expensive and is centrally funded via Renal Units, Royal Preston Hospital Renal Unit expenditure on EPO exceeds £1,000,000 annually. It is money well spent.

Dr. Simon Gibson

MOLECULAR STRUCTURE OF RECOMBINANT HUMAN EPO (Hu Epo)

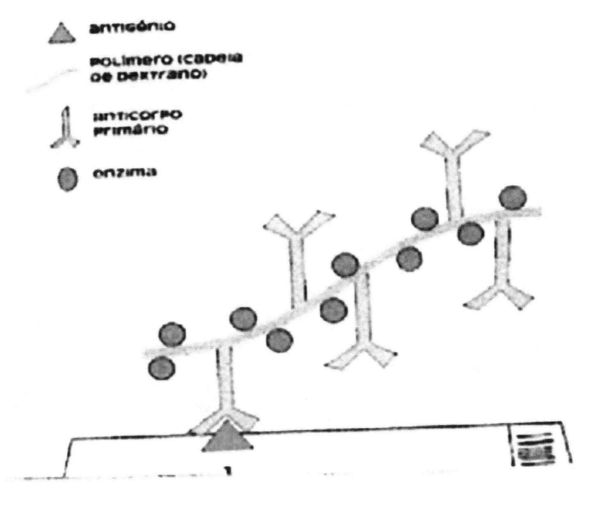

ERYTHROIPOIETIN (EPO)

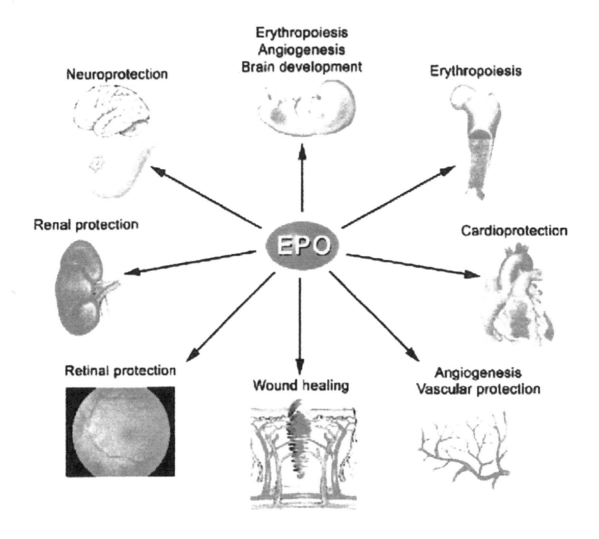

INTERSTITIAL CYSTITIS

A GP phoned me on a Wednesday afternoon, asking me to see one of his patients urgently. As I had a Lancaster clinic the next day, I said she could be over-booked on to the clinic. She was a 29 year old teacher who lived in I, quite a long distance from Lancaster. But if you want the best, you have to be prepared to travel !!

She was suffering from dreadful urinary frequency associated lower abdominal (tummy) pain. She was having to visit the bathroom every 30 minutes or so. Day and night, but her urine diptest was negative.

This puzzled me greatly, and I immediately consulted the popular online management tool that we had available at RPH (See vignette Mid Morning Coffee or Tea ?? page 59). My tentative diagnosis was Interstitial Cystitis, also known as "Painful Bladder Syndrome". I had never seen a case before.

I duly saw this lady in Lancaster the next day. She was clearly unwell, and even had to leave my consulting room during the consultation to visit the toilet. Her urine diptest was clear. She warranted a full abdominal and pelvic assessment. I explained what was necessary (see To Swab or Not to Swab). My clinic nurse would act as chaperone. My nurse took her into an examination cubicle, and when the patient was appropriately undressed and draped and positioned, I joined them in the cubicle.

Her vulva and introitus appeared normal, but she had marked abdominal tenderness. Pelvic examination revealed severe bladder tenderness. I left the examination cubicle. When she rejoined me in the consulting room, I discussed with her what I thought the problem was. I indicated that other possible pathology would need to be excluded. I thought she had Interstitial Cystitis, or Painful Bladder Syndrome.

A variety of investigations were requested. (abdominal x-ray, pelvic ultrasound, cystoscopy, blood tests, more urine tests etc etc.). I offered her immediate admission to RLI, but she understandably declined. It would have been extremely embarrassing for her. Nevertheless, I gave her the direct phone number of my Lancaster Secretary.

She was over- booked onto my next RLI clinic (next week).

At her next clinic, she was possibly a little better, but abdominal and pelvic examination did not confirm this.

We discussed possible treatments. I was not keen on any of them. Neither was she. We agreed that a policy of Wait and Watch (or "Masterly Inactivity") was appropriate. I would see her weekly, repeating abdominal and pelvic examinations.

All her investigations, including cystoscopy, were unremarkable.

Her symptoms improved, and her bladder tenderness on pelvic examinations settled. The frequency of follow up was reduced. After 6 months, her symptoms had settled completely. I did a final pelvic examination, which was unremarkable. And as she left clinic, I said I hoped that I would not need to see her again. She laughed !!

EVERY POTENTIAL DIALYSIS PATIENT
IS CAREFULLY ASSESSED

For those unlucky enough to have kidney problems and declining kidney function, the prospect of dialysis (artificial kidney treatment) looms large.

Providing information about what might be ahead is vital. Hence the "Dialysis Education Team". The Team consists of a highly skilled dialysis nurse or sister, a renal dietician, and a social worker (if possible). The potential dialysis patient would usually be assessed at home. With the patient's permission, members of his/her family could be present.

The various dialysis modalities would be discussed: haemodialysis in a renal unit, home haemodialysis, peritoneal dialysis (see vignette One Kidney Two Kidneys Three Kidneys Dialysis Transplantation, page 39).

The renal dietician (a dietician who has a special interest in kidney failure) would explain what changes in diet would be required as kidney failure advanced.

IF YOU LIKE EATING MUSHROOMS DO NOT GET KIDNEY FAILURE Why? Because mushrooms are very high in potassium, and a high serum potassium, 7 or above, can cause cardiac arrest.

There are other forbidden foods: fish, leafy green vegetables, raisins, chocolate, avocados, cooked tomatoes, etc. etc. etc. Why? Because they are high in potassium.

LoSalt a table salt substitute is absolutely forbidden, Why? Because KCl has been substituted for NaCl (see vignette No Salt or Lo-Salt. That was the Question, page 30).

The Team was asked to see a highly intelligent 90 year old in Lancaster, who was aware that his kidneys were failing, and he did not want to die of kidney failure. He had an excellent GP, who fully complied with the Morecambe Bay Renal Referral Guidelines. After much discussion, it was decided that he would start haemodialysis in Preston (the main dialysis centre) and then if he was well enough, could move to the Kendal Satellite Unit. He would need to have an arterio-venous (AV) fistula created (see vignette: The Aeterio-Venous Fistula ?? The Route to Heaven).

But all our efforts were in vain. Sadly this delightful man had a cardiac arrest before his AV fistula could be created. RIP.

Dr. Simon Gibson

SOMETIMES IT IS USEFUL TO HAVE A MEANDERING MEDIC ON THE TEAM

This vignette is from when I was Senior Registrar (SR) in Nephrology (N) and General Medicine (GM) at Bristol Royal Infirmary.

I was working in the General Nephrology Clinic headed by my boss, Prof. T Feest.

As ever, it was busy.

I was allocated the case-notes of a seemingly well-developed teenager who had been suffering from loin pains. Her GP considered that her pains might be kidney in origin.

A medical history was taken. And then something clicked in my thoughts. Could this teenager be pregnant with an ectopic pregnancy??

If missed, a ruptured ectopic pregnancy can result in death.

A menstrual and sexual history was taken (never usually done in a kidney clinic). The young lady was sexually active and on the contraceptive pill. But she had suffered a tummy upset recently.

My concerns increased dramatically. A tummy upset can prevent the absorption of the pill. I asked for part of her urine sample to be sent to the lab for an urgent pregnancy test. However it was going to take approximately 36 hours for a result to come through.

I went and spoke to the outpatient Sister and explained my concerns. The teenager needed an urgent USS (ultrasound scan) to assess her pelvic contents and while we waited for that, I needed to give her a pelvic examination (a PV examination).

The Sister agreed with me. She accompanied me to my clinic room, and I explained to the teenager my concerns. She was an intelligent girl and gave her consent. Accordingly I left the clinic room while Sister ensured the teenager undressed below the waist, brought her legs up and let them flop apart. Of course she was draped. Sister then invited me back into the clinic room and I proceeded to perform a PV pelvic examination. Clinically there was no evidence of an ectopic pregnancy.

The next day she attended for an Ultrasound Scan (USS) of her pelvic contents. And the result of the pregnancy test came through.

The teenager was pregnant, and thankfully the USS confirmed my PV findings that the pregnancy was not ectopic.

I had taken the phone number of the teenager and phoned her to inform her of the USS and pregnancy test results.

She said she did not want to continue with the pregnancy. I explained that she needed to make an urgent appointment to see her GP. I said that I would phone her GP to make sure she was given an urgent appointment.

The system in Bristol was that all terminations were requested by GPs. It was not within my remit (or Prof. Feests') to arrange terminations. This was GP territory and rightly so. GPs are better placed to provide counselling pre-termination, and essential follow up post-termination.

I pondered. Would a SR in N and GM, without my meandering background, have considered the possibility of pregnancy and ectopic pregnancy? A stint of 6 months Obstetrics and Gynaecology is not part of Nephrology training.

The following week in the N Clinic, The OPD Sister came over to me and said I had looked after the pregnant teenager with care and compassion. And she had informed Prof Feest to that effect.

Sometimes it is useful to have a meandering medic on the team !!

MID MORNING COFFEE OR TEA ??

This vignette dates from my time as Registrar/ Research Registrar at East Birmingham Hospital (EBH). It is now Birmingham Heartlands Hospital.

The main staff route into EBH took you along the management corridor. Here there was always a gorgeous aroma of freshly brewed coffee.

My duties regularly took me into the Out Patients Department (OPD) to assist in clinics.

One day, I was doing a morning clinic. It was always busy and overbooked. Mid clinic (10.30 to 11.00) our clinic nurse would bring us a plastic cup of instant coffee or tea. Of course we paid for it. The clinic did not stop. We "slurped while we worked". The fluid and caffeine kept our "grey brain cells" alert and possibly improved productivity.

That day, the usual drinks service stopped. Why ?? The clinic nurse said "orders from a macho manager".

The medical staff were surprised and irritated as there had been no prior discussion about the change.

I was back in OPD the next day. So, around 10.30-11:00, when a consultation finished, we "downed tools" and adjourned to the Doctors' Mess for a coffee/tea break. We returned to OPD 10-20 minutes later.

Result: total chaos in the OPD.

24 hours later, normal drinks service was resumed.

What had motivated this macho manager? Was he an early environmentalist concerned about plastic cup usage? Did he think we stopped work for a drinks break? Was he concerned about the drink spilling and damaging a computer keyboard? Did he think that EBH paid for the drink?

Heaven only knows.

HEY BIG SPENDER

I confess, I was a big spender. Of NHS money.

In fact all nephrologists (kidney specialists) are big spenders of NHS money. Once a Consultant Nephrologist has decided that a patient should have dialysis, it commits the NHS to significant expenditure.

These decisions involve many individuals, but it is the Consultant who makes the final decision.

The costs of haemodialysis vary slightly according to location, provider etc. etc. but a rough estimate of the costs involved are:

A single haemodialysis session (4-6 hours duration) costs £200-£300.

This usually happens 3x weekly, cost £600-£900.

For 52 weeks these figures scale up to £31,200-£46,800.

On top of this there are transport costs to the dialysis unit, medication, out-patient attendances etc. etc. etc. etc.

These costs are ongoing until the patient receives a kidney transplant, or dies.

Costs are reduced if the patient has their own dialysis machine at home.

Peritoneal dialysis costs are usually lower.

Did I ever feel guilty about spending the NHS's money in this way? Absolutely not.

The song Hey Big Spender was written by Cy Coleman and Dorothy Fields.

Dr. Simon Gibson

THE PEARLY GATES PURGATORY JUDGEMENT DAY HEAVEN

What might happen to Dr X ??
What might happen to me ??

Dr X and Judgement Day

I have no knowledge of his personal life, apart from that he has a son.
I can only comment on his professional life. Before he became somewhat self obsessed, he was a good Doctor, and obeyed THE RULES.
I think he would get through the Pearly Gates, but would need to spend significant time in Purgatory before entering Heaven.

Me and Judgement Day.

I think I would get through the Pearly Gates both from a personal and professional standpoint. Of course I would need to spend time in Purgatory. But would I need to spend more time in Purgatory than Dr X ?? Difficult. No comment.

REVELATION 21:21
GENESIS 2:4
2 NEPHI 9:4

DOCTOR AW OR PROFESSOR AW ??

DEFINETLY PROFESSOR AW

At last I had a colleague to help me with my workload.

AW is German, and he climbed the greasy pole of career advancement in Medicine and Nephrology at Hanover Medical School.

He was a fine colleague. Exceptionally bright. Brilliant at IT (I was not !) and an excellent clinician.

He aspired to be Professor AW.

As we are all aware, Germanic efficiency is often to be admired (try shopping at Aldi).

To become Professor AW, he had to follow the strict rules of Hanover Medical School (HMS). He had to write X number of research papers, attend Y number of conferences etc. etc.

Quite different from how a UK Professor is appointed.

Doctor AW achieved his goal and was appointed Professor AW by Hanover Medical School.

But RPH would not recognize his Professorship. Why? Allegedly because his Degree had not been awarded by a UK university.

How arrogant and facile I thought.

And so whenever I wrote to, or introduced patients to him, I made a point of always calling him Professor AW.

Ironically, the authorities in Morecambe Bay (Lancaster, Kendal, Barrow) were more than happy to recognize his Professorship. They respectfully addressed him as Professor AW in all correspondence etc. etc.

Many years later, when I told my brother and sister-in-law about this arrogant farce, my sister-in-law cynically suggested that if RPH recognized his Professorship, they might have to pay him more.

Dr. Simon Gibson

A SLIP OF THE TONGUE

It was my Wed AM clinic at RPH, and it was as busy as ever.

I invited a 44 year old new patient into my consulting room. The appearances of the patient were unusual; the patient was genotypically male but phenotypically female.

He/she was 5 ft. tall, had beard stubble, long hair but was wearing a skirt.

For humans:

GENOTYPE is the genetic makeup of an individual, the genetic code, eg DNA, susceptibility to disease etc.

PHENOTYPE is an expressed and observable trait e.g. hair colour, length of hair etc.

(Downloaded from Diffen via Bing)

As per normal, I asked about the patients' PMH, DH, etc.

Inadvertently during the consultation I called the patient "Mr", and he/she went berserk, called me sexist, misogynist, and walked out of the consulting room.

What had I done wrong??

The patient was transitioning from male to female, and I had inadvertently addressed he/she as "Mr".

Within 24hrs he/she had made a formal complaint about my conduct.

The sad thing is that he/she had very significant kidney failure, approximately 80% loss of kidney function. And if no reversible cause was found, he/she would now be on dialysis or transplanted or dead.

And what of the complaint?? I apologised for my slip of my tongue.

URINE DIPSTIX

I am a great fan of urine dipstix. For a patient with kidney issues they are essential, see vignette "Sterile Urine Sample Bottles", page 66.

Thankfully Amazon has solved supply issues. Looking on-line today (15.9.20), for around £10, it is possible to buy 150 urine reagent dipstix.

I keep my own supply: see photo of my supply.

Why am I so enthusiastic? They are inexpensive, give rapid answers, and are simple to use. In spite of statements like "you have to be a healthcare professional to use them", which I find patronizing in the extreme, for my patients, the only contra indication is colour blindness.

A small, fresh sample of urine, is captured in a sterile urine pot, the stick is dipped in, and within a few seconds, hugely important information is available.

Most important of all, is the infection screen. For those with impaired kidney function, an infection can precipitate emergency dialysis if not acted upon immediately. If a patient has the slightest twinge of an infection, they can use a dipstick to screen, if +ve, a formal MSU (Mid Stream Urine) MUST be done and sent to the path lab for analysis.

The stix can screen for a variety of other pathologies. Put urine dipstix into an internet search engine and enjoy !!!

Dr. Simon Gibson

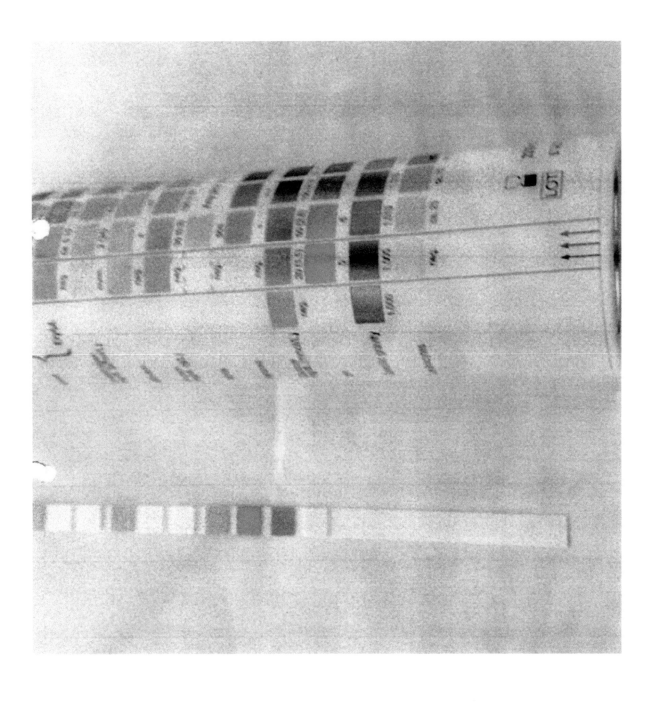

STERILE URINE SAMPLE BOTTLES

You will struggle to understand this vignette.

For renal (kidney) clinics, patients were expected to bring a small, fresh, sterile urine sample with them. The sample would then be tested in OPD.
Obviously, to do this, a small, sterile urine container is required. Such sample bottles were usually obtained from their GP surgeries.

It is easier for everyone to pass urine in quiet privacy at home. Hospital OPDs are often noisy, unfamiliar and stressful places.

The cost of such sample bottles is small.

However some GP practices refused to provide sample bottles. Some started charging patients for them. This was only an issue in Dr X's catchment area.

Why did some GP practices behave like this? Difficult.
Possibly because small expenses add to become large expenses which eat into practice profits. And profits mean Porsches (see vignette The Porsche Index).
Possibly because these GPs were ignorant of the importance of such samples This comes back to Dr X's failure to educate effectively the GPs in his catchment area.

How did we deal with this crazy situation? RPH was obliged to provide the sample containers.

Dr. Simon Gibson

MR TIM FARRON, MP TO THE RESCUE.

All doctors want the very best treatment for their patients.

I had been seeing a fairly complicated lady in her 50s in my Kendal Clinic. She lived about 40 miles from Kendal, in a small rural village.

Then one day, while reading a medical journal, I spotted a new drug that would help her. It had passed all regulatory tests. But like most new drugs, it was very expensive.

I approached the Hospital Pharmacy about getting supplies of the new drug. No was the answer. Why? No money was the answer. I tried pleading, and asked her GP to write a supportive letter. He was more than happy to oblige. Still the answer from Pharmacy was NO.

So I turned to Mr Farron, the patients MP, for help.

Within days, previously locked doors opened, barriers were lifted, and the Pharmacy agreed that the patient could have the new drug.

The arrangements were fairly complicated. I would write out the necessary prescription, the Hospital Pharmacy would dispense it, and the new drug would be sent by special delivery to the village pharmacy, and the patient would collect it along with her routine medication.

The drug manufacturers suggested precautionary blood tests every month. Her very supportive GP was more than happy to help and take the blood samples, then he and I scrutinized the results. No problems.

The patients' condition improved. Then after being on the drug for about 4 months, she un-expectantly passed from a totally separate problem. RIP.

I had to seek Mr Farrons' help on a few other occasions. Every time he responded within an hour or so, and the problems disappeared within a week or so.

THANK YOU MR FARRON.

But should it be such a struggle to secure supplies of life transforming new drugs ??

A MARS BAR AN HOUR

This vignette relates to the 1980s. I qualified in 1981.

My first employment was at Rotheram District General Hospital. It was a 6 month Pre-Registration post in surgery.

Rotheram was a steel town. The hospital was situated on the edge of the town, surrounded by green fields. It was only 30 minutes drive from Sheffield. Very importantly the staff residences were spacious and there was more than adequate parking. My car at that time was a blue Citroen 2CV. House Officers lived on-site.

The staff canteen had a very good reputation. So much so that HGV drivers passing along the motorway would divert off, park in the extensive car parks, and visit the Hospital Canteen !!

My second 6 month Pre-Registration post was at the Royal Hallamshire Hospital Sheffield, doing General Medicine. It involved a lot of kidney medicine. Once a kidney Doctor, always a kidney Doctor !!

Successful completion of these posts was mandatory to achieve Full Registration ie become a "proper Doctor".

A contractual feature was mandatory on-call out of hours work. The hourly rate of pay was pitiful and equated to A MARS BAR AN HOUR.

Dr. Simon Gibson

THE PORSCHE INDEX

It was my Friday afternoon clinic at Kendal hospital.

A man in his early 40s had been referred because of increased blood pressure (BP). I endeavoured to take his medical and social history (routine). However, he made a sales pitch for Porsche cars!! He was the local Porsche sales manager.

He went into great detail about all the local GPs that owned Porsches.

I was interested and decided to research the issue. So began the Porsche Index. I enlisted the help of my patients. It was a bit of fun, and a good way to put patients at their ease. I wanted to know how many GPs in my catchment area (Morecambe Bay) had Porsches.

I suspected that many GPs would use their "other" or "plebeian" car for practice work. The Porsche would be reserved for trips to church, the bank, the restaurant, the golf club, etc etc. I asked those that had agreed to help in the study to "spy" on their GP, and try and establish if they had a Porsche.

The results trickled back. And I was surprised at the large number of GPs that had Porsches. You are probably wondering what sort of car I have. A mid-range Ford Focus.

Recently my GP visited me at home on a non medical matter. And what vehicle did he arrive in? Yes, a top of the range Porsche (he was the Senior Partner in the practice). We had a chat about cars. I asked him how much his annual Road Tax was: £385. I told him how much I paid: £20.

Of course GPs have every right to spend their hard earned salaries on whatever they like. And they do work hard. As hard as Hospital Doctors ?? No comment.

I remembered that my 0+ G boss (see vignette Whistle in the Wind?? Yes. Whistle on the Ward?? Definetly Not !! page11). had a Porsche. As a Christmas present we had bought her a toy model Porsche to put on her mantelpiece!!

MUNCHAUSEN'S SYNDROME

This was never an issue for me or any other nephrologist.

It is very easy to check if a person has impaired kidney function. A simple blood test is all that is required.

There is a parameter in the blood called "creatinine" and this is easy to measure in a laboratory. It is related to the muscle mass of an individual and their kidney function.

There is a derived parameter called the e-GFR (Glomerular Filtration Rate), which is calculated from the serum creatinine, and this gives an estimate of kidney function.

I preferred to use the serum creatinine, look at the patient, and make my own estimate of the e-GFR, I was usually much more accurate than the laboratory e-GFR. But it took a few years of kidney medicine to acquire the skill.

So if anyone is concerned about their kidney function, simply ask your GP to check your serum creatinine or e-GFR.

I wish that all of kidney medicine was this simple. Sadly it is not.

HOME-MADE CAKE IN MY ROYAL PRESTON RENAL CLINIC

I had been referred a 17 year old young lady because her BP was surprisingly high for her tender years.

Also her kidneys were leaking more protein than they should do (excess proteinuria).

A detailed history was taken, including social history. She was a trainee chef at a local catering college.

I conducted a physical examination. Her mum acted as chaperone. Nothing of note was found.

The diagnostic process involved me performing a Renal Biopsy. This is not a very pleasant procedure (suggest you put Renal Biopsy into a search engine), but is absolutely essential if a firm diagnosis is to be made.

It turned out that she had IgA (Immunoglobin A) nephropathy, which entirely fitted with her elevated BP and proteinuria. (oh dear, more homework, suggest you look it up on internet !!).

The outlook for such patients is very variable. Some are hardly troubled, in others it is more severe. Another of my patients, Distinguished Professor of Medical Statistics at Lancaster University (Peter Diggle) progressed to end stage renal failure, and needed dialysis then transplantation. Thankfully his brother donated him one of his kidneys, so he was only on dialysis for about 6 months. Incidentally, Peter helped me with my MD statistics.

Those with IgA nephropathy need life long follow up by a nephrologist. The incidence of the condition is very low.

I took advantage of my young trainee chef patient !! I managed to persuade her to bake a cake for all who helped out in my clinic. And what a cake it was !!!! Multi-layered sponge, no marzipan (I do not like marzipan).

Thankfully her condition progressed slowly, and she only needed 6 monthly follow up.

I did not have the nerve to ask her for another cake.

MULTI LAYERED SPONGE CAKE

(NO MARZIPAN)

MY ADMISSION TO ROYAL PRESTON HOSPITAL (RPH) FOR A LUMBAR PUNCTURE (LP) AND SPINAL FLUID PRESSURE MEASUREMENTS

To try and find out what was going wrong with me, my neurologist, Dr JN and my neurosurgeon, Mr A had arranged my admission to Ward 2B (one of the Neuro-surgical wards at RPH).

RPH is a regional centre for Neurosurgery. At the last count I think it has about 10 neurosurgeons. It has an outstanding reputation. When I worked at RPH, I was a frequent visitor as many of the neurosurgical patients had some degree of renal impairment. And I think then there were only 3 Consultants providing the service. As in Renal Medicine, they were massively overstretched.

I was asked to attend as a day case on 09.05.2019. With one thing and another, I was not discharged until 11.05.2019. See collage of pictures, which I downloaded from Bing Pictures. My LP was expertly done by one of the Neurosurgical Registrars, and I hardly felt a thing, and I have a very low pain threshold!!! And whingeing threshold??? No Comment.

As a leaving present, the Occupational Therapy Department gave me a solid aluminum walking stick (I already had a much inferior cane version that I had bought myself). My aluminum stick was my "third leg". It was very important to me. And I became very anxious if it was not next to my side.

Thank you. Thank you Ward 2B.

Lumbar Puncture

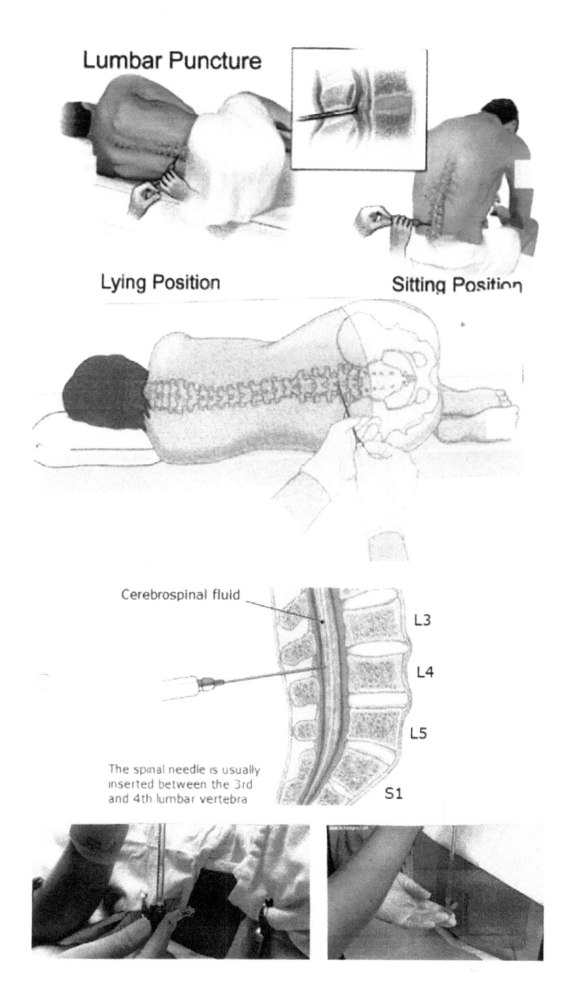

Lying Position

Sitting Position

Cerebrospinal fluid

L3

L4

L5

The spinal needle is usually inserted between the 3rd and 4th lumbar vertebra

S1

THE BIG DAY (4.12.19)

Blood tests were done, head CT scan was done and head MIRI was done, radiology multi-disciplinary team had passed their verdict: I had hydrocephalus (water on the brain) see figure of Hydrocephalus and a Ventriculoperitoneal (VP) shunt. These were downloaded via Bing.

I needed neurosurgery, and at 06.30hrs. on 4.12.19, Tes (my best friend) and my daughter (S) collected me from my home and Tes drove us down to Royal Preston Hospital Neurosurgery Department. Tes and S waited with me until I was summoned into the pre-operative ward and a Consultant Anesthetist put me to sleep, and inserted an ETT (Endotracheal Tube) into my trachea, and connected me to a ventilator to maintain my respiration while under general anesthesia GA.

Mr A and his team then drilled a hole in my skull, and fitted a venticulo-peritoneal shunt, connected it to a drainage tube tunneled under my skin leading down to my peritoneal cavity so the excess cerebrospinal fluid could drain away. See fig downloaded via Bing.

When I came round from the GA I was on Ward 2B, and my brother Mark was at my bedside. He had travelled up from his home in Oxford the previous day.

I was an in-patient for three days, and then Mark took me back to my home in Lancaster, and he headed back to Oxford.

And I began my recovery. I had probably got all my National Insurance contributions back in one go !!

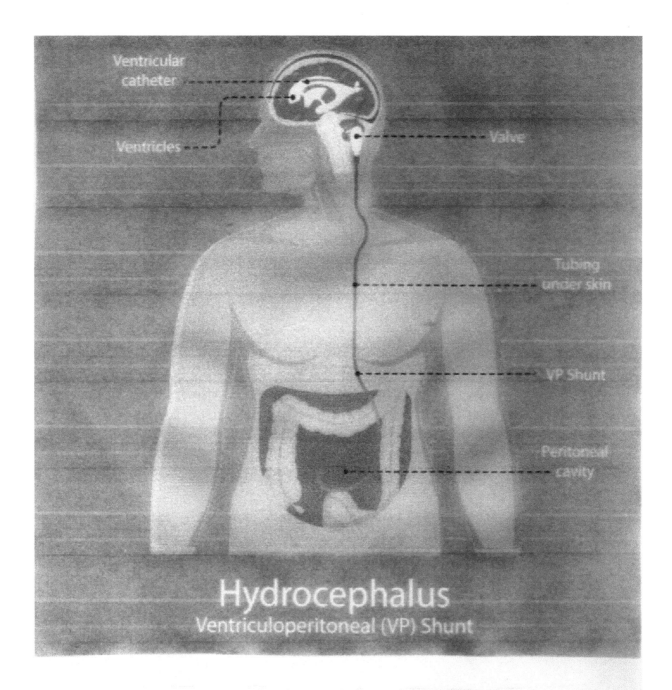

Hydrocephalus
Ventriculoperitoneal (VP) Shunt

Ventriculoperitoneal (VP) Shunt

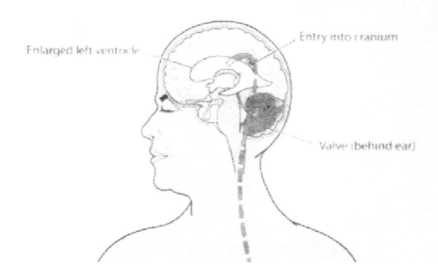

MY RECOVERY FOLLOWING NEURO-SURGERY ON 4.12.19

The first thing that I noticed was the improvement in my legs. The awful stiffness had decreased. This improvement was progressive, and soon I was able to put my trousers on without difficulty.

Life around the house was difficult (I live alone). I needed my trusty walking stick to help me walk from living room, to kitchen, to downstairs toilet etc. My walking stick was a physical and mental aid. A few falls makes you paranoid about falling again. The stairs were difficult, but I managed.

My driving license was suspended for 6 months. I knew this would happen, and I accepted it. Better to have lifesaving neuro-surgery, a driving suspension for 6 months, than die.

At my worst, I needed walking stick in my right hand, and a sturdy adult to support my left side, or I fell over, or I thought I was going to fall (my anxiety again).

My walking and balance improved. And then came a landmark day. I felt sufficiently confident to go out on my own with just my sturdy NHS walking stick. Soon after that, with further improvement, I felt sufficiently confident to walk unaided. AND I NO LONGER NEEDED TO USE A WALKING STICK.

Walking outside in the glorious surroundings of South Lancaster is an activity I really enjoy. I would walk along wooded glades to the Lancaster Canal, and then walk along the towpath into Lancaster. When in Lancaster city centre, I would do some shopping, and reward myself with tea and cake at a favourite café.

During one of these walks, I met my GP, Dr GA. Our children used to play together and we were colleagues and friends. He saw the immense improvement in my physical condition. He asked if there was anything that I needed help with. I said I was struggling to communicate with the DVLA. I wanted to be sure that DVLA returned my licence on 4.6.20, when my 6 month suspension would be up.

So Dr GA "took up the cudgel" on my behalf with DVLA

I would not be true to myself, if I did not say that I found parts of the DVLA to be the most selfish, self-seeking, self-serving, ego centric, self opionated, egotistical, ego maniacal, self absorbed, narcissistic, INCOMPETENT, dis-courteous, avaricious, self-opionated, egotistical, egomaniacal, self absorbed, narcissistic, heubristic, covetous, vain, arrogant, disengenuous, disdainful, disobliging, disengaging, dismissive, disgraceful, disgusting, disinterested, dishevelled, disillusioning, disorganised, cowardly, craven, dispassionate, Government Agency that I have ever had the misfortune to interact with.

And our taxes pay their wages.

After mounting a sustained e-mail and snail-mail campaign, I managed to get my license back, almost 2 months late.

I copied all e-mails through to my hugely supportive MP, Ms Cat Smith.

I had been in lockdown for 8 months. No fun.

Recently I found my higher cerebral function was improving. This made sense as all that excess fluid which was squashing my brain would not selectively squash the neurons that control my legs. The neuro-surgery at Royal Preston Hospital had removed all that excess fluid permanently .

Now I am almost back to my "new normal".

And I can jump into my car, whenever I like, and go to my favourite local cafes. HAPPY DAYS!!!!!

THANK YOU THANK YOU NHS, THANK YOU ROYAL PRESTON HOSPITAL THANK YOU MY GPs THANK YOU ALL THOSE NUMEROUS OTHERS FOR HELPING ME,

GET MY LIFE BACK

Dr. Simon Gibson

MORBID OBESITY

From: Simon Gibson
Sent: 25 July 2020 14:36
To: SMITH, Cat
Subject: FW: LIFE DEATH OBESITY

Sent from Mail for Windows 10

From: simop@tiscali.co.uk
Sent: 25 July 2020 14:32
To: julie.lennard@dvla.gov.uk
Cc: Medadviser@dvla.gov.uk
Subject: LIFE DEATH OBESITY

Irritating me again. Another medical vignette from my working life. Very topical.

This is probably of no relevance to current interaction with DVLA. But am listening to ball by ball cricket commentary and watching TV, and can e-mail simultaneously. Am a male multi-tasker!! I am also writing a monograph titled "Tales of a Meandering Medic" and this case will feature.

You may find it interesting, if tragic. RTAs are tragic.

A 21 year old care worker who was massively obese was referred to my General Medical Clinic for consideration of anti-obesity surgery. Obesity is a complex issue.

Several weeks of assessment was required, including visits to psychologists and dietitians In due course she was accepted for surgery and she was duly admitted to Royal Preston Hospital under the care of a Consultant Surgeon.

As was policy, she was given prophylactic heparin (a blood thinning agent) to prevent blood clots.

This was stopped the night before surgery as per policy. During that night she had a cardio respiratory arrest and despite valiant efforts to revive her, she passed.

Postmortem showed a massive pulmonary embolism (blood clot stopping circulation through heart). RIP.

Dr S P Gibson

THE ESSENCE OF ME

To Dr Gibson,

*Now you're retired
it's time to have
the time of your life!*

*Congratulations
and Enjoy Yourself!*

With very best wishes for a
long and restful retirement!

Dean Barker and family.

From the 1st time I met you in 1998, you have always been honest and highly supportive.

When people are taken ill, it is crucial that they are in the care of someone whom they trust and have complete faith in. I am one of the lucky patients who found that in you.

I hugely appreciate the way that you have advised me over the years and the way that you have allowed me to take control of my own lifestyle.

I have always enjoyed our appointments in so many ways: they have always been frank & honest, fun and amusing, but best of all realistic and appreciative of my need to not allow my transplant to run my life.

I am still some years from the exit door from the blackboard (now whiteboard!) jungle but I know that I can continue to enjoy my life, living it to the hilt in every way I can.

Thank you + very best wishes,

COURTESY... I THINK IT MATTERS. DO YOU?

Listed below are some definitions of courtesy:

Courtesy "the showing of politeness in one's attitude and behaviour towards others" (downloaded from Bing)

Synonyms: politeness, courteousness, good manners, civility, respect, respectfulness

Courtesy n "polite behaviour, or a polite action or remark" (downloaded from the Cambridge English Dictionary via Bing)

Courtesy n "good manners, courteous behavior" The Concise Oxford Dictionary OUP, my own copy

Examples of what some might consider to be dis-courteous behaviour:

1. I wrote to a Ms Julie Lennard CEO of the DVLA, basic salary £96,000, on 12.5.20. I have not yet received a reply 08.10hrs. 6.10.20
2. I e-mailed a Charlie Massey CEO of the General Medical Council, basic salary £250,000 at 05.58 on 28.9.20, because I was very concerned about the behaviour of a wayward Dr., a Dr Sarah Brown, an employee of the DVLA. I asked Mr Massey to act within 72hrs. It is 08.21hrs. 6.10.20, and I still have not had a reply.

Mr Massey is not medically qualified. I am a very experienced Doctor, and more than capable of spotting a rogue Dr like Dr Sarah Brown.

I am very highly qualified:

Dr SP Gibson BA MB ChB MA MRCP FPCert T(GP) MD FRCP

Some might say that Mr Massey is not just discourteous, he is arrogant and incompetent, and completely failing in his duty to protect the public from incompetent Drs like Dr Brown, and failing to maintain the integrity of the medical profession.

TODAY IS 28th MARCH 2021.
AND STILL NO REPLY THESE "CEO"NEED TO LEARN SOME MANNERS
READER DO YOU AGREE?

THE PROOF POSITIVE EVIDENCE

When I was out walking on 9.6.20 by chance I met my GP, Dr Andy Gallagher.

We exchanged pleasantries.

He asked about my recovery from neurosurgery on 4.12.19.

I replied remarkable. Leg stiffness gone. Balance improved. My neurosurgeon had told me that my balance would take the longest time to improve.

Any headaches?

I said the only headache I had was the DVLA.

Why? Andy asked.

I told him that the DVLA was ignoring my requests for them to return my driving licence. It should have been returned on 4.6.20, six months after my neurosurgery on 4.12.19.

Andy replied sometimes they could be a bit tardy. He said he would see what he could do and would copy me into his e-mail conversation with the "Drivers Medical Group" (DMG). These were "Doctors" who assessed an individual's fitness to drive.

And so, on 10.6.20 at 08.56 hours, Andy contacted the DMG by e-mail to try and persuade DMG to return my driving license.

AND HE COPIED THE e-mails TO ME
AND HE COPIED THE e-mails TO ME
AND I WAS AMAZED

The "doctor" who was assigned my "case" was more concerned with her own convenience than my welfare, and the return of my driving license. Please see overleaf for copies of said e-mails.

I decided to refer her to the Gang of Mealy-mouthed Charlatans, previously known as the General Medical Council. See Glossary.

I sent the GMC copies of the e-mails, with a letter expressing my concerns about the behaviour of Dr SB.

And they impugned my integrity, ignored the proof positive evidence, and in-effect called me a "liar." However the Gang of Mealy-Mouthed Charlatans will get their come-uppance soon. The GMC has a governance body: the Public Standards Authority for Health and Social Care (PSAHSC). I have submitted the Proof Positive Evidence to them, and other evidence which clearly shows that the GMC has behaved very badly.

I discovered the PSAHSC myself. By putting the words "governance body GMC" into an internet search engine.

The GMC did not tell me about the PSAHSC. This fact alone shows that the GMC knows that it has messed up, it has failed to discipline a wayward Dr., and it has failed to maintain the integrity of the medica profession.

These failures should result in the PSAHSC recommending:

1. The loss of Charitable Status for the GMC.
2. The immediate resignation of the current members of the GMC.

There is a desperate need for reform within the GMC organization. There needs to be a new organization in which transparency is mandatory. No more totally lacking in transparency foddecisions@gmc-uk.org

Nobody in this life is above scrutiny. The Prime Minister has to answer questions in the House of Commons and has to appear before Parliamentary Select Committees.

The new GMC must be prepared to admit that it can make mistakes.

And it must never again behave badly towards someone like me, who has far more qualifications than any individual member of the GMC, and has vastly more frontline clinical experience than any of them.

Until this happens, the letters GMC will mean:

Gang of Mealy-mouthed Charlatans
Gag-bag of Mealy-mouthed Charlatans
Gunga of Messey Charlies
Gang of Messey Charlies
Group of Messey Charlies
Good Mulched Compost
Gang of Moonies and Croonies
Gang of Morons Chuntering
Gazebo of Muttering Chums
Pastiche of Pompous Pillocks PPP oops but PPP does provide a very good description of the GMC.

RE: Advice 6m following shunt
Gallagher Andrew (P81002) Lancaster Medical Prac... <u>andrew.gallagher@gp-p81002.nhs.uk</u>
10/6/2020 8:56

Thank you Sarah
It sounds like he has had some letters backwards and forwards without making much progress;
he submitted his form D1 on B1 on 19 May.
His details are:

Dr Simon Gibson
12 Craiglands Court
Aldcliffe
Lancaster
LA1 SAU
DOB 4 March 1954
Tel 01524 381924

This is my last day at work for the time being so I have taken the liberty of coping Dr Gibson
in to this e-mail.

Many thanks again for your help with this matter

Your sincerely
Andrew Gallagher

From: medadviser [mailto:Medadviser@dvla.gov.uk (mailto:Medadviser@dvla.gov.uk)]
Sent: 10 June 2020 07:53
To: Gallagher Andrew (P81002) Lancaster Medical Practice
Cc: medadviser
Subject: RE: Advice 6m following shunt

Dear Dr Gallagher

Thank you for your further email.

Due to the coronavirus crisis DVLA has had to reduce services due to limited workforce. It sounds like your patient is struggling because of this.

If he has previously told DVLA about his condition then there should be a medical case already in our system.

As a practical way forward if your patient was to consent for you to give me his details (full name, date of birth, address) I could access his case and ask my administrative colleagues to send out the relevant paperwork to him.

Kind regards.

Dr Sarah Brown
DVLA Doctor

---

from: Gallgher Andrew (P81002) Lancaster Medical Practice [mailto: Andrew.Gallagher@gp-p81002.nhs.uk
(mailto: Andrew.Gallagher@gp-p81002.nhs.uk)]
Sent: 09 June 2020 14:51
To: medadviser
Subject: RE: Advice 6m following shunt

Thank you
Sorry, should have been clearer
He already notified the DVLA when he got it done but is struggling to notify you that he is now past the 6 month stage.

From: medadviser [mailto:Medadviser@dvla.gov.uk (mailto:Medadviser@dvla.gov.uk)]
Sent: 09 June 07:25
FW: Advice 6m following shunt
Gallagher Andrew (P81002) Lancaster Medical Practice andrew.gallagher@gp-p81002.nhs.uk
10/6/2020 15:30

Hi Simon
Not sure she copied you in...

From: medadviser [mailto:Medadviser@dvla.gov.uk (mailto:Medadviser@dvla.gov.uk)]
Sent: 10 June 2020 11:52
To: Gallagher Andrew (P81002) Lancaster Medical Practice
Cc: medadviser
Subject: RE: Advice 6m following shunt

Dear Dr Gallagher,

Thank you for providing the details of your patient.

I have accessed his records at DVLA.

One of my DVLA doctor colleagues has been involved in Dr Gibson's case and recently reviewed his case. I have sent them a copy of these emails so they are aware of the situation.

I have checked with my administrative colleague and it appears the issue is awaiting for the relevant documents that Dr Gibson has sent in to be scanned onto the case. Unfortunately until this is done I am unable to move this case forwards.

I do note that Dr Gibson has stated he is a keyworker and there is a process in place to prioritize keyworkers in the current climate. If he sent the paperwork in recorded or special delivery there may be opportunity for the administrative team to locate his paperwork quickly.

Kind regards.
Dr Sarah Brown
DVLA Doctor

FREE SPEECH? NOT WITH THE D-V-L-AUTOCRACY

Reader, this vignette will amaze you.

Simply look at a copy of the e-mail I was obliged to send to Preston Magistrates Court on 02.08.20.

The wisdom of keeping copies of everything !!

And our taxes pay the (?? inflated) wages of the D-V-L-AUTOCRACY.

02/08/2020   apps.talktalk.co.uk Compose
From   simop@tiscali.co.uk
To   lancsmagslisting@justice.gov.uk   CC BCC
CC   cat.smith.mp@parliament.uk

MORE DISGRACEFUL BEHAVIOUR OF DVLA/DRIVERS MEDICAL GROUP (DMG)

I wish to report to the Court that the behaviour of the DMG towards me has reached a new low.

THEY ARE TRYING TO DENY ME FREE SPEECH.

I have been attempting to engage the DMG in an e-mail conversation. The purpose of this was:

1. To inform DMG of the impact that late return of my license (should have reached me by 04.06.20) was having on me.
2. To provide the doctors on the DMG with some medical education.

I must immediately stress that these e-mails were neither offensive nor abusive. They were copied through to my local MP, and she would have disciplined me if they were.

What did DMG do ? THEY BLOCKED MY E-MAIL ADDRESS (simop@tiscali.co.uk (mailto:simop@tiscali.co.uk)

I suspected that DMG might behave in such a childish way and so I had a back up G mail address (gibsonsimon301@gmail.com (mailto:gibsonsimon301@gmail.com)) ready.

I resumed 1 and 2 but a few days later my G mail address was blocked.

PLEASE EXPEDITE THE DATE OF THE APPEARANCE OF DVLA/DMG IN PRESTON MAGISTRATES COURT.

Dr S P Gibson BA MB ChB MA MRCP FPCert T(GP) MD FRCP
Retired Consultant Physician and Nephrologist

PS I hope you are not working today!

https://apps, talktalk.co.uk/appsuite/#!!&app=looxmail/compose compose

THE SWANSEA IVORY TOWER
HOME OF THE DVLA

THE SHAMEFUL LETTER

On 16.7.20 I received a letter from the "Drivers Medical Group" (DMG), a small department in the Driver and Vehicle Licensing Agency (Autocracy), dated 13.7.20.

It surprised me.

Why?

1. It impugned the integrity of my neurosurgeon, Mr A.
2. It impugned the integrity of the neuro-surgery department at Royal Preston Hospital.
3. It was exceptionally patronising towards myself.
4. It implied that I was ignorant of the vital importance of an individual being medically fit before driving a motor vehicle.

I will explain:

In the second paragraph of the letter, DMG states "We have written to Mr. A, Neurosurgery, Royal Preston Hospital, however due to the ongoing situation with Covid 19, we are not expecting a reply within the next 12 weeks".

How long did it take for Mr A to reply? 4 days.

Further into the second paragraph, DMG states "I hope you can appreciate that we need to write to your doctor/consultant to ensure that they do not have any concerns that your medical condition affects your ability to safely control your vehicle at all times".

In fact, I had been involved with medical fitness to drive issues for 25 years. These whippersnapper "doctors" were probably in nappies when I began my Consultancy at Royal Preston Hospital.

I wonder if any member of DMG had been asked to see a patient on an ICU. I had on many occasions, often the patient had been involved in an RTA, and had damaged his/her kidney function.

Driver & Vehicle Licensing Agency

Dr Simon Peter Gibson
12 Craiglands Court
Aldcliffe
LANCASTER
LA1 5AU

32085

Driver and Vehicle Licensing Agency
Drivers Medical Group
Swansea SA99 1DG
Phone: 0300 790 6806   Fax: 0300 083 0083
Website:
www.gov.uk/driving-medical-conditions

Our Reference: M39082914/Tm13lvl1

Date: 13 July 2020

Dear Dr Gibson,

PROGRESS UPDATE ON OUR MEDICAL ENQUIRIES

I am writing to keep you updated on the progress of our enquiries.

We have written to Mr Ansar, Neurosurgery, Royal Preston Hospital, Sharoe Green Lane, Fulwood, PRESTON, PR2 9HT, however, due to the ongoing situation with Novel Coronavirus (COVID-19), we are not expecting a reply within the next twelve weeks. I hope you can appreciate that we need to write to your doctor/consultant to ensure they do not have any concerns that your medical condition affects your ability to safely control your vehicle at all times.

As soon as we are in receipt of the information we will write to you to let you know further progress. You only need to contact us if you have new information for us to consider, such as a change in the above medical professional's details.

If you wish to see our standards of service you can do so by viewing www.gov.uk/driving-medical-conditions/what-happens-after-you-tell-dvla or
https://www.gov.uk/government/publications/inf94-customer-service-guide-for-drivers-with-a-medical-condition

Rev Mar 20

Yours sincerely,

Drivers Medical Group

ACKLETTC

M 39082914
Page 1 of 2

ANOTHER SHAMEFUL LETTER FROM THE DVLA

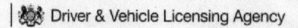 Driver & Vehicle Licensing Agency

Complaints Team
Driver and Vehicle Licensing Agency
Longview Road
Morriston
Swansea
SA6 7JL

Phone:	0300 790 6806
Website:	www.gov.uk/dvla
Our Ref:	S02765453/M39082914
Date:	27 January 2021

Mr Simon Gibson
Flat 11 Goring Lodge
Pegasus Grange
White House Road
Oxford
OX1 4QE

Dear Mr Gibson

Thank you for your letter of 11 January about your driving licence. I have been asked to reply.

As the holder of a valid driving licence you have a legal responsibility to update your licence with your new address. The necessary D1 form to complete and return with your current licence was enclosed with our previous letter of 29 December 2020. Please either complete and return this form with the details of your new address or complete the process online via the following link - https://www.gov.uk/tell-dvla-changed-address.

Arrangements are now being made to unblock the two email addresses that you previously used to make multiple approaches to the Drivers Medical Group. However, please be aware that if you persistently misuse this service in the future, then this will no longer be an available option for you.

Yours sincerely

Mark Pitman
Complaints Team

Find out about DVLA's online services
Visit: www.gov.uk/dvla

 **INVESTORS IN PEOPLE** We invest in people Gold

 disability confident EMPLOYER

Mr Mark Pitman   Flat 11
Complaints Team   Goring Lodge
DVLA   Pegasus Grange
Morriston   Whitehouse Road
Swansea SA6 7JL   Oxford OX1 4QE

Dear Mr Pitman
I have received your letter of 27.1.21.

-I take exception to your statement that I misused e-mail access to the Drivers Medical Group DMG). I DID NOT. The contrary is true... THE DMG TRIED TO DENY ME FREE SPEECH, by blocking simop@tiscali.co.uk and then four days later gibsonsimon301@gmail.com. But DVLA/ DMG could not stop me using old style letter writing and using the postal service.

We live in a democracy, not a fascist state. You and your colleagues would do well to remember this. Monolithic organizations cannot do as they please.

The DVLA/DMG behaved disgracefully.

Their shameful conduct will be exposed to a wide audience within the next 3 months. Enclosed with this letter is a copy of the front-sheet of Dame Julie Mellor's report on the DVLA published in 2016. You should study it and learn from it.

My interaction with DVLA/DMG clearly shows that the current hierarchy have not learned from Dame Julie Mellor's report.

The DVLA/DMG ignored me. They ignored my MP (MS Cat Smith). But they could not ignore the Courts. I think it was the impending appearance in Preston Magistrates Court that made DVLA/DMG behave.

I will not hesitate to use the Courts in the future. If DVLA/DMG misbehave again.
The motoring public pay the wages of DVLA/DMG through income tax and motoring taxes.
The current hierarchy of DVLA/DMG have bitten the hands of those that feed them for too long.
For me, the DVLA is the DVLAutocracy.

Dr S P Gibson BA MB ChB MA MRCP FPCert T(GP) MD FRCP
Retired Consultant Physician and Nephrologist

cc. Ms Anneliese Dodds MP
cc Ms Julie Lennard CEO DVLA

DITHER AND DELAY AT THE DVLA

When the going gets tough
The tough NHS staff get going
Some have died
And I cried

And what of DVLA?
They back away
Must protect their 8 hour day
And have a corona virus holiday

Phone off hook
Websites blocked
I am shocked
All so DVLA can play
And have a corona virus holiday

Whippersnappers they are
And have damaged my car
They think they can ignore me
But they cannot ignore the Courts
Hiding away in their Swansea Ivory Tower
What a shower

Why not work from home?
Oh no said a little gnome
DVLA likes to play
And have a corona virus holiday

Are they busy ??
No way
Are having a corona virus holiday

I was a frontline worker
And no shirker

My medical referees but a phone call away
So why the delay ??
DVLA are having a corona virus holiday !!

Local MP (Cat Smith) to the rescue
Oh no says DVLA
We want to play. And have a corona virus holiday
No chance says super dynamic Cat
You must earn your pay
AND STOP HAVING A CORONA VIRUS HOLIDAY

Bottom feeders they are
And have damaged my car

I have been asked to return to the fray
So please return my license today
AND STOP HAVING A CORONA VIRUS HOLIDAY

If overcrowding is the problem
Why not introduce
A 3x8hr shift system
And then only a third of staff
Will be in the Ivory Tower at one time

Oh no says DVLA
That would interfere with our play
And having a corona virus holiday

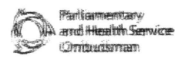

Driven to despair

How drivers have been let down by the
Driver and Vehicle Licensing Agency

Foreword

This report highlights major failings in the way the Driver and Vehicle Licensing Agency (DVLA) makes decisions about whether people with certain medical conditions are safe to drive.

We have upheld investigations into eight separate complaints where people with complex medical conditions were unfairly prevented from driving, sometimes for several years, as a result of flawed decisions, significant delays, poor communication and complaint handling. We have seen the significant impact that DVLA's actions have had on people's lives: causing them to lose their jobs, be cut off from friends and family, and suffer significant stress and frustration. DVLA has accepted our findings and recommendations for all eight cases and in six of them has granted the licence applied for, thereby overturning its own original decision.

Our outstanding concerns are two-fold. First, that there will be others who have experienced the same injustice and hardship for whom things have not yet been put right. Secondly, that insufficient action has been taken, or is planned, to prevent the same failures being repeated and impacting many more people in the future. In particular, further action is needed to improve the robustness of assessments of fitness to drive for people with certain medical conditions and disabilities.

Without this, there are risks that people fit to drive will be denied a licence to do so, and others, who pose a risk to the public and themselves, will keep their licence and continue to drive. In coming to our view we have considered evidence, reinforcing our concerns, from a range of organisations and individuals including the Department for Transport's own Independent Complaints Assessors, the British Medical Association, the International Glaucoma Association, eminent specialists in the area of vision and many driving groups and charities.

The Department for Transport has accepted our findings about the failures we have identified. I am deeply concerned, however, that it has not accepted our recommendations to put things right by providing justice for everyone who may have been affected or by improving the robustness of the criteria applied in future medical assessments.

As a result, I am publishing this report in the public interest and laying it before Parliament under Section 10 (4) of the *Parliamentary Commissioner Act 1967*.

Dame Julie Mellor, DBE
Parliamentary and Health Service Ombudsman

October 2016

Parliamentary
and Health Service
Ombudsman

Driven to despair

How drivers have been let down by the Driver and Vehicle Licensing Agency

Presented to Parliament pursuant to Section 10(4)
of the Parliamentary Commissioner Act 1967

Ordered by
the House of Commons
to be printed on 19 October 2016

HC 660

Print ISBN 9781474137072

Web ISBN 9781474137089

Printed in the UK for the Williams Lea Group on behalf of the
Controller of Her Majesty's Stationery Office

ID P002832200   10/16

Printed on paper containing 75% recycled fibre content minimum

ADDENDUM 1

From: simop@tiscali.co.uk
Sent: 11 June 2021 18:43
To: James Lappin
Cc: Simon Gibson
Subject: Re: Our client: General Medical Council

Fieldfisher
17th floor 1 Spinningfields 1 Hardman Street
Manchester M3 3EB

Dear Sir

I have made a brief study of your letter.

You have completely neglected to mention the Proof Positive Evidence that I submitted to the GMC concerning the behaviour of a wayward Doctor, a Doctor Sarah Brown, an employee of the DVLA, who works on the Drivers Medical Group.

I would also point out that I am now an advisor to the Professional Standards Authority for Health and Social Care. This is the governance body of the GMC.

Please ask the GMC to provide you with a copy of the Proof Positive Evidence.

If they have (? conveniently) lost it, you will be able to read it in my Memoir "Tales of a Meandering Medic".

The publisher of my Memoir is Book Trail Agency, 8838 Sleepy Hollow Road, Kansas City, MO 64114, USA.   The United States Library of Congress Control Number is 2021906971.

I am a bit obsessional about record keeping. I print off every e-mail before I send it, and I also print off the sent e-mail. And I never delete important e-mails.

Without the slightest doubt, the GMC has failed to discipline a wayward Doctor (Doctor Sarah Brown), and has therefore failed to maintain the integrity of the Medical Profession.

Although I am retired, I still care about these matters.

I am also in contact with the Charity Commission (my contact is Jenny Stewart, PPS to Baroness Stowell).

My Memoir will be published in the next 2-3 weeks. The cost of the e-book format is $3.99, and the paper format $9.99.

Professor Harnden is prominent on BBC TV, and also practices at Morland Medical Centre in Wheatley, which is about 20 miles from my home. So he is my local member of the GMC.

His behaviour towards me has been disgraceful. I have e-mail and paper records to prove this.

Has he not told you about his disgraceful behaviour ? Or has he (? conveniently) omitted to do this.

I ceased contact with Professor Harnden about a week ago.

I will print off this e-mail and send it to you by Post Office Recorded delivery. And of course I will keep a copy.   I will also inform the Professional Standards Authority for Health and Social Care, the governance body of the GMC.

Yours faithfully
Dr S P Gibson BA MB ChB MA MRCP FPCert T(GP) MD FRCP
Retired Consultant Physician and Nephrologist and GP and Oxford University Laboratory Scientist.

Dr Simon Gibson
Flat 11
Goring Lodge
Pegasus Grange
Whitehouse Road
Oxford
OX1 4QE

17th floor
1 Spinningfields
1 Hardman Street
Manchester M3 3EB

T +44 (0)161 835 8010
F +44 (0)161 835 8015
E info@fieldfisher.com

www.fieldfisher.com

By Post
By Email (simop@tiscali.co.uk**)**
(simonpetergibson@yahoo.com)

Our Ref: JL5/TM12/UK01-000492-16384/96925429 v1

James Lappin
Partner
+44 (0)161 835 8001 (Direct Dial)
+44 (0)7796 144 402 (Mobile)
james.lappin@fieldfisher.com

EXTREMELY URGENT

15 June 2021

Dear Sir

Our client: General Medical Council ("GMC")
ALL ELECTRONIC COMMUNICATION NOW BLOCKED

We write further to our letter dated 11 June 2020, in which we informed you that we had been instructed to act for the GMC and its Council Members in order to protect them from harassment by you. In particular, this harassment took the form of you inundating the GMC and its Council members with correspondence and documents by email and by post. We required you to immediately cease and desist from continuing with such behaviour.

In response to our letter, you sent a series of further emails to the GMC. Furthermore, this firm (Fieldfisher) has now also been inundated with vast numbers of emails from you, together with attachments and other documents sent by you electronically. This is in addition to numerous other pieces of correspondence and other documentation sent by post, including (this morning) a 'Wanted Poster' with our Mr Lappin's photograph on it, which is intimidating and totally unacceptable.

Furthermore, rather than confine your correspondence to the writer (Mr Lappin), you have directed (and/ or copied) such emails to a vast number of Partners and other employees of Fieldfisher, who are entirely unconnected with this matter. It is to be inferred that you have simply obtained email addresses of such other members of the firm from publically available records online. Sending emails to Partners and other employees (or copying them in) in circumstances in which they have no knowledge of this matter or connection to it is also entirely inappropriate and unacceptable. This is of course exacerbated by the sheer number and inappropriate content of such communications.

This behaviour clearly amounts to harassment of this firm (and its members and employees) for the purposes of section 2 of the Harassment Act 1997, which is a criminal offence. It is absolutely unacceptable and must cease immediately.

In the event that you continue to behave in such manner, we shall take steps to protect this firm and its members and employees, including seeking injunctive relief and damages and/ or reporting your conduct to the Police for investigation.

ELECTRONIC COMMUNICATION BLOCKED:-

In any event, this firm has now taken the step of immediately blocking all forms of electronic communication from you or directed by you.

Any further emails or other forms of electronic communication sent by you to this firm or any of its members or employees will be blocked, they will not be received and they will not be read by anyone from this firm.

POSTAL CORRESPONDENCE:-

You may continue to correspond with this firm in relation to this matter **only** by Post, directed (**only**) to Mr Lappin at Fieldfisher LLP, 17th Floor. No.1 Spinningfields, 1 Hardman Street, Manchester M3 3EB.

You must not send any correspondence or documents relating to this matter to any other member or employee of this firm.

Any post directed to any other member or employee of this firm will not be read or considered, and will immediately be destroyed.

Yours faithfully

Fieldfisher

Fieldfisher LLP

ADDENDUM 2

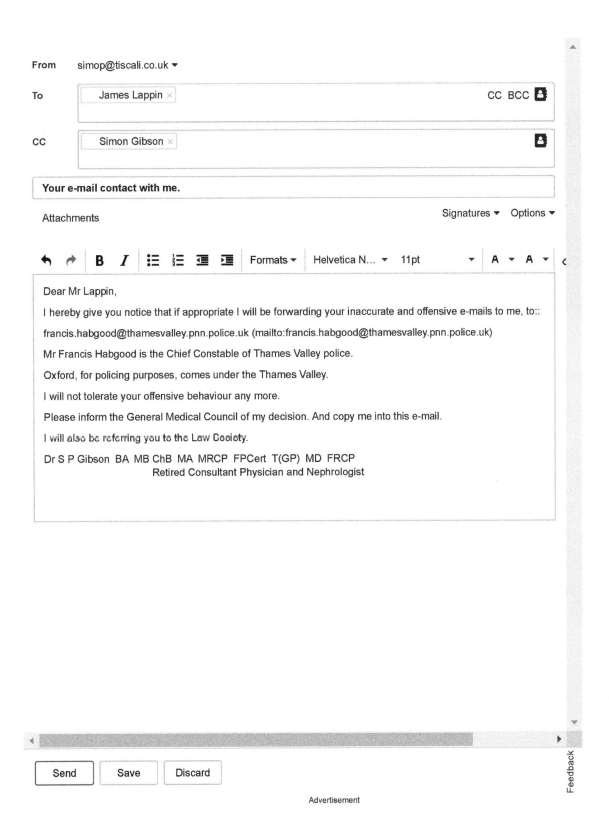

From   simop@tiscali.co.uk ▾

To | James Lappin × | CC BCC

CC | Simon Gibson × |

Your e-mail contact with me.

Attachments   Signatures ▾   Options ▾

↰ ↱ **B** *I* ☰ ☰ ☰ ☰ Formats ▾ Helvetica N... ▾ 11pt ▾ A ▾ A ▾

Dear Mr Lappin,

I hereby give you notice that if appropriate I will be forwarding your inaccurate and offensive e-mails to me, to::

francis.habgood@thamesvalley.pnn.police.uk (mailto:francis.habgood@thamesvalley.pnn.police.uk)

Mr Francis Habgood is the Chief Constable of Thames Valley police.

Oxford, for policing purposes, comes under the Thames Valley.

I will not tolerate your offensive behaviour any more.

Please inform the General Medical Council of my decision. And copy me into this e-mail.

I will also be referring you to the Law Society.

Dr S P Gibson BA MB ChB MA MRCP FPCert T(GP) MD FRCP
                   Retired Consultant Physician and Nephrologist

Send   Save   Discard

Feedback

ADDENDUM 3

LAPDOG LAPINN

HE AIN'T CLAPPIN NOW
BUT I AM

LAPDOG LAPINN
LAPDOG LAPINN

HE AIN'T CLAPPIN
BUT I AM

HE WORKS FOR A GANG OF
SOLICITORS IN MANCHESTER CALLED
FRESHFIELDFISHER.

THEY AIN'T CLAPPIN EITHER

LAPINN WAS SO "ECONOMICAL" WITH
THE TRUTH, THAT SOME MIGHT SAY
HE WAS LYING

WHAT DO I SAY ???
NO COMMENT

HIS "PARTNER" IN CRIME WAS A GP
NAMED NEDNRAH, WORKS AT
DNALROM MEDICAL CENTER, IN
YELTAEHW.

YELTAEHW IS ONLY 20 MILES FROM
MY OXFORD HOME.

SO NEDNRAH IS MY LOCAL MEMBER
OF THE "GANG OF MEALEY-mouthed
CHARLATANS", FORMERLY KNOWN
AS THE GENERAL MEDICAL
COUNCIL

LAPDOG LAPINN

LAPDOG LAPINN
HE AIN'T CLAPPIN NOW!!!!!
BUT I AM +++++++

BEACAUSE LAPPIN IS A LAPDOG OF
THE GMC

LAPDOG LAPPIN
LAPDOG LAPPIN

LAPINN AND CRONIES (THE GMC)
CHOSE TO IGNORE THE PROOF
POSITIVE EVIDENCE

AND THE FACT THAT I AM NOW AN
ADVISOR TO THE PROFESSIONAL
STANDARDS AUTHORITY FOR HEALTH
AND SOCIAL CARE, THE GOVERNANCE
BODY OF THE GMC

LAPDOG LAPINN

LAPINN LAPINN

HE AIN'T CLAPINN
NEITHER IS
FRESHFIELDFISHER
THEY ATTEMPTED TO PERVERT THE
COURSE OF JUSTICE

SO THEY WILL ALL GO TO JAIL FOR A
VERY LONG TIME. AS WILL THE GMC
AND LAPDOG LAPINN

OOHRAH OOHRAH
JUSTICE FOR ME
SEMPER FI FOR ME.
BUT NOT FOR THE GMC AND LAPDOG
LAPINN

LAPDOG LAPINN

Dr. Simon Gibson

LAPDOG LAPINN
HE AIN'T CLAPPINN
BUT I AM

AND RIGHTLY SO
AND RIGHTLY SO

BECAUSE I AM HONEST
BECAUSE I AM DECENT

I AM VERY HIGHLY QUALIFIED: BA
MB ChB MA MRCP FPCert T(GP)
MD FRCP.
FAR BETTER QUALIFIELD THAN
NEDNRAH, AND ALL OTHERS ON THE
GMC.

THE ARROGANCE OF THE GMC IS
AMAZING. THEY THINK" GOD" IS
THEIR ASSISTANT. THEIR HUBRIS IS
OFF THE SCALE

LAPDOG LAPINN
LAPDOG LAPINN

HE AND THE GMC AIN'T CLAPPIN
HE AND THE GMC AIN'T CLAPPIN

BUT I AM

Dr. Simon Gibson

ADDENDUM 4

HUMPTY HARNDEN

HUMPTY HARNDEN HAD A GREAT
FALL

ALL THE KING'S HORSES AND ALL THE
KING'S MEN

DECIDED NOT TO PUT HARNDEN
TOGETHER AGAIN

THEY SAID HE IS SUCH AN ARROGANT
MAN

AND HE THINKS GOD IS HIS ASSISTANT
SO THEY DUMPTED HIS PIECES IN A
BIN

"GOOD RIDDANCE"

WE HAVE GOT RID OF THE MOST
ARROGANT GP ON THE PLANET

ANOTHER ONE OF THE KING'S MEN
SAID PUT HIM IN A BIG ROCKET

AND BLAST HIM INTO OUTER SPACE

A FITTING END FOR THE MOST

ARROGANT GP ON THE PLANET AND
POSSIBLY IN THE SOLAR SYSTEM TOO
SO GET HIM GONE

STRIKE HIM OFF THE GENERAL
MEDICAL REGISTER

SEND HIM TO JAIL FOR ATTEMPTING
TO PERVERT THE COURSE OF JUSTICE
WITH HIS CRONIE LAPDOG LAPINN

A DISGUSTING AND DISGRACEFUL
PAIR THEY ARE

Dr Harnden is a GP member of the General Medical Council.

To see a picture of Dr Harnden: put Members
General Medical Council into an internet
search engine.

Lightning Source UK Ltd.
Milton Keynes UK
UKHW050953100921
390301UK00006B/113